"I came with you willingly," she said casually, "to remind you of a few things."

"Such as?" He edged a leg closer, without yet touching her.

"Such as, new babies make for impossible love affairs."

"Difficult, yes."

"And ladies who've just had babies have healing stitches. In awkward places."

He smothered a laugh.

Laura kept the deliberately light tone, but her eyes were serious, suddenly filled with anxiety. "Owen, there are lots of women out there. Women with time, women with nice flat stomachs . . . I deeply appreciate what you've done for me. You've just . . . been there, through a rough week, and I—"

"You foolish woman. If you really believe the only thing going on between us is a mutual-support society, we'd better clear that up right now."

Owen's head dipped down . . .

Jeanne Grant

Jeanne Grant is a native of Michigan. Married with two children, she and her husband raise cherries and peaches on a farm near Lake Michigan. A graduate of Michigan State University, she worked as a counselor, teacher, and personnel manager before devoting her time to writing. She sold her first book to SECOND CHANCE AT LOVE on December 8, 1981. "I remember the date well because the next day was my birthday," she says, "and I was afraid to answer the phone for fear they'd changed their minds."

Writing involves her whole family. "The kids would probably be shocked if they had dinner on time, but they're more than willing to help me do research...from making chocolate, to mining silver, to exploring the ghost towns of northern Idaho."

Last year Jeanne won the Romance Writer's of America Silver Medallion Award and the Romantic Times Award for sensual writing.

Dear Reader:

Set on a mystery buff's tour, *Lovers and Pretenders* (#310) by Liz Grady pairs brash, wily, and slightly mysterious Jake Latimer with soft-spoken Catherine Hollis, a librarian who devours whodunit's on the sly and who's dying for a chance to play super sleuth in real life. Actual mystery cleverly interlocks with mock murder and mayhem, but Liz Grady never lets lapse the towering emotional power of Jake and Catherine's love. A wonderfully inventive, heart-stopping romance by a masterful talent.

Sweets to the Sweet (#311) by Jeanne Grant is as delicious as it sounds. I'm sure many of you will identify with Laura Anderson, an anxious new mother for whom everything is going wrong! Her milk won't flow, the baby keeps crying, the house is a wreck, and now she's smashed her car into someone's outrageously expensive classic Austin-Healey! Luckily for Laura, Jeanne Grant provides a *very* satisfactory hero to save the day. Chocolate manufacturer Owen Reesling knows all about caring for babies—and he's terrific at soothing a distraught mother ... Once again Jeanne Grant brings you a fresh and delightful love story told with her soul-satisfying blend of humor and poignancy.

Ever Since Eve (#312) by Kasey Adams features *two* sets of lovers—one from the younger generation, and one from across the "gap." Optimist Linda Dawson openly admits to matchmaking for her darling mother Ruth, but handsome Paul Tanner suspects the mother-daughter team of gold-digging. He's furious when his friend Simon falls for Ruth, and he's even more flummoxed by his own magnetic attraction to Linda! Here's a hilariously mixed-up foursome who prove it's glorious to find love at any age.

If you've ever tried to interpret "other-worldly" signs and portents, you know the dilemma facing the heroine of *Blithe Spirit* (#313) by Mary Haskell. Guided by a mischievous Ouija board, vacationing executive Linda Chester waltzes into the arms of the impossibly handsome male "destined" to be the love of her life—and immediately discovers that things—and hero Paul Phillips—aren't always what they seem. Spiced with puzzles and liberally laced with humor, *Blithe Spirit* will make you dizzy with delight.

Don't miss *Man Around the House* (#314) by Joan Darling. When Meg Lambert reluctantly agrees to rent a room to Boone Bradshaw—a maverick from Missouri with a down-home manner and a heart as big as all outdoors—she gets much more than she bargained for. Boone invades her house, makes himself at home, and generally threatens to take over her life! Meg's determined to bounce him—but instead finds herself eagerly anticipating their cozy evenings together. Of course she won't admit she's falling hard for this lovable giant—and her stubborn resistance provides half the fun in this exuberant and unpredictable love story from a real pro.

Happily driven to laughter is what you'll be when you read *Driven to Distraction* (#315) by wonderfully funny new writer Jamisan Whitney. Innocently outrageous Andee Rotini and gorgeous-but-stoic Thor Engborg don't have a whole lot in common. Andee craves fast food, while Thor thrives on tofu. Thor has all the answers, while Andee relies on her six lovingly protective brothers for advice. So why does Jamisan Whitney force these two opposites into a cramped motor home and send them across the great Southwest? Because she knows they're going to drive each other crazy in the most hilarious and sensually exciting ways possible! I guarantee you'll be utterly charmed—or I'll eat Thor's tofu!

Happy reading! Warm wishes,

Ellen Edwards

Ellen Edwards, Senior Editor
SECOND CHANCE AT LOVE
The Berkley Publishing Group
200 Madison Avenue
New York, NY 10016

Second Chance at Love

SWEETS TO THE SWEET

JEANNE GRANT

**SECOND CHANCE AT LOVE
BOOK**

SWEETS TO
THE SWEET

- 1 -

A TEAR DRIBBLED down Laura's cheek. Glancing in the rearview mirror, she brushed it away impatiently.

Of all the ridiculous. . . . If she'd wanted to fall apart, she'd had plenty of chances over the last year. When she was two months pregnant and filing for divorce from Peter, she hadn't cried. When she was eight months pregnant and simultaneously trying to move, buy a house, and set up her business, she hadn't cried. When Mari had arrived two weeks early, she admitted to a few indelicate screams, but no blubbering. When, weak as a kitten, she'd brought the baby home, only to remember that no fairy godmother had stocked the house with food or unpacked

1

the rest of her furniture, she hadn't cried.

At least on those occasions, she'd had good excuses. She certainly didn't have time to fall apart now. To make things worse, the welling tears were blinding her on a day already marked by poor visibility. Rain was too mild a description of the conditions outside. Deluge was more appropriate. Noah's ark time.

A sleek Austin-Healey pulled into the road in front of her, old, elegant, and in mint condition. Laura had nothing specifically against vintage Austins, but the driver was obviously determined to crawl along at a snail's pace. She cast a frantic glance at the baby beside her.

The infant seat was cushioned in pink angora. Mari was dressed in a spotless white bunny suit and covered with a hand-embroidered blanket in pink and white. From the soft fluff of blond hair to the perfect miniature fingers and toes, the baby was still a source of wonder for Laura. Mari was a little red-faced. She was always a little red-faced when she screamed bloody murder. The piercing wails shattered somewhere near Laura's eardrums like the sound of despair.

The louder the baby cried, the more tears sneaked down Laura's cheeks.

She *had* to get the baby to a doctor. She'd taken Mari's temperature four times that morning. The baby didn't have a fever; she was fed, warm, dry, and, God knew, loved. There was nothing in the baby books about an infant who ate like a lumberjack, slept like a stone, and screamed the rest of the time. Something had to be *terribly* wrong.

While trying to soothe the infant with one hand, Laura jammed a foot on the accelerator. Water spit behind the tires of her ancient Pinto. White oaks bordered both sides of the rolling country road, their bark shining, their leaves glistening like emeralds. Connecticut was ... wonderful. Especially in early summer. Woods and hills and history—it was the kind of place in which Laura had always wanted to live, the kind of home she wanted for Mari. The ravine behind her house was blanketed with wood hyacinths and wild lilacs, and at night the stars nestled down close to the treetops, almost touchable.

Last year had been hell, but at least it was over. Laura had everything she wanted and needed to put her life back together—Mari, a home, and her work. Now, if the baby would stop crying...

The green light in the distance turned amber, then red. Laura automatically started to brake, and then Mari let out a frantic muffled yell. Her tiny fists had been flailing; she'd managed to cover her face. When Laura leaned over to grab the blanket, her foot slipped from the brake to the accelerator. She caught less than a second's glimpse of the Austin looming in front of her.

Her first and only instinct was to throw herself over the baby. The taste of tin flooded her mouth as a spine-jarring jolt shuddered up her vertebrae, followed by the sound of shattering glass and metal climbing on metal. Brakes screamed in the distance.

The silence was more sudden than the crash.

Violently trembling, Laura pushed herself up, her attention focused only on the baby. Mari's big blue eyes stared at her peaceably. A hiccup followed. Straightening, Laura smoothed the baby's blanket with shaky hands and inhaled huge gulping breaths. Her throat was clogged with a gigantic lump of mixed guilt, horror, and relief. Mari wasn't hurt— no thanks to her mother.

Grabbing her purse, Laura pushed at the door. Either it was jammed or she didn't have the strength of a marshmallow. She tried again, and the door flew open. Big, fat drops of rain immediately saturated her white lace blouse and dampened her disheveled hair. A streak of lightning darted into the treetops; thunder bellowed in the distance. Her legs didn't want to support her. She made them.

Her Pinto's front end was crushed like used tinfoil. The back of the Austin-Healey had fared better, but it was no longer in mint condition. She ignored the cars the way she ignored the rain, jogging toward the driver's door of the other vehicle.

She wrenched it open, her heart nearly stopping when she saw the dark-haired man slumped over the steering wheel. "Oh, God..." He moved, and she breathed again. "You're all right? I can't tell you how sorry I am. I...oh, you've got a little cut on your forehead." She pulled a clean folded diaper out of her purse and began dabbing at the tiny streak of red.

"Lady."

He didn't exactly *knock* her hand away, but it was a definite push. Her first glimpse of his face was of dark gray eyes, as friendly and volatile as black fire. A slash of jet brows hooded the rage in those eyes. Barely.

She had only seconds to form an impression. He was a dark, striking man with a thick pelt of short hair, wearing an expensive gray suit that strained to fit his shoulders. Thirty-five? A blade of a nose set off chiseled cheekbones and a stubborn jaw. Control joined with intelligence and lines of authority in his features. His mouth was compressed in an uncompromising line.

Maybe sometime in the far future she would be fascinated by the way those features were put together, but not now. Now, the only impression that registered was his anger, and nobody that mad could be hurt too badly.

"I'll be right back," she said swiftly, and darted off to her own car. Mari had started crying again. Laura reached in to soothe the infant. Her hands were badly trembling as they gently caressed her daughter's cheek. The pulse hammered in her throat, refusing to slow down. "Don't cry," she said desperately. "Please, darling, please..."

Her head jerked up for another crash of thunder. There was no way she would expose Mari to the storm. Taking one last glance at the baby, she raced back to the stranger's car. Two long legs were gingerly climbing out of the driver's seat. Standing, the stranger was an imposing head taller than she was, and at a rough guess, carried two hundred pounds of irritation to back up that height.

"You *are* all right," she said in a rush. "Look,

this is all my fault and I'm terribly sorry, but if your car's still running, could I possibly borrow the keys?"

"What?"

She dragged a hand through her hair. "I don't blame you for being irritated, but you don't understand—"

"Lady. You just plowed into my car."

"Yes. I know that. And if I were alone, I wouldn't be asking you, but Mar—never mind." She cast another frantic glance at her car, then abruptly shoved her purse in his stomach. "Look, I just don't have time to explain. In there. You can have it all. There's some money, the keys to my house. Credit cards . . ." Again, she shoved the dripping light brown mane away from her face. "You can have everything. Really. And I just need your car for a few minutes; I swear I'll have it back to you—"

"You're *crazy!"*

"I *need* your car."

"You'll drive this car when hell freezes over." He immediately added, *"Maybe."*

"Look. I can't just stand here arguing with you . . ."

She darted off again, the wind tossing her skirt around her bare legs. Owen shook his head, trying to clear it. He was used to solving tough business problems, and as if by reflex his heart was already pumping adrenaline, his mind consolidating options . . . but this situation *was* a little different from the ones he usually faced. Even in the worst crisis between New York and Brazil, he could at least count on his adversaries' being rational.

And his forehead hurt. In the crash, his temple

had connected with the reading glasses he'd stuck behind the visor. As he rubbed the growing welt above his left brow, his eyes narrowed on the woman's slim form as she bent into her car.

He guessed her age at twenty-five, and she was wearing some kind of high-necked lace blouse that reminded him of a cameo. Earlier, when she'd tried to smother him—she'd clearly never had a course in first aid—he'd caught the smell of hyacinths. And rain. Her oval face had been a pale blur, but he still carried the image of incredible turquoise eyes, framed by a dark spray of lashes and delicately arched brows.

At the moment, all he could see was the feminine curve of her hip and slim white legs jutting out of the car. A frown pleated his forehead. The woman was clearly irrational, and that bothered him. Absently, he catalogued the delicate features, the long, rich hair curled to her shoulders, the determined chin, and—from somewhere—had an impression of intelligence and pride. In the business world, Owen had learned to do a quick read on people. This woman just didn't strike him as someone who was habitually irrational.

In the three long strides it took him to reach the back of his car, he decided she might be one of those people who simply overreacted in a tense situation. Inspecting the damage to his Austin-Healey, he was tempted to do the same.

The beautiful antique car was the first toy he'd allowed himself in a very long time, and he'd just finished his first drive. The gleaming chrome didn't even have a fingerprint. The sleek beauty hugged curves the way silk clung to a woman's body, soared responsively at his slightest touch, and purred when pushed to the limit. His darling was now crumpled chrome and glass, and though the dent could be fixed, the once-perfect suspension system would never be the same.

The woman rushing toward him was treated to the dangerous silence that regularly terrorized his boardroom.

"My car won't run," Laura said helplessly.

"No kidding?"

"Look—"

"Did you even consider slowing down for the red light?"

"You're angry. Believe me, I don't blame you, but I have to get my baby to the doctor!" Huge turquoise eyes tilted up to his, far too distraught to see his sudden change in expression.

"Wait a minute. You didn't say anything about a baby before."

"I've been trying to. You were so angry—"

"She was hurt in the accident?"

"No, it has nothing to do with that. All day she's been crying, and I . . . she's ill; I know she's terribly ill. I've been so frightened, and—" Her head jerked up when she heard the wail of a police siren, and she gave the stranger a frantic glance. *"Please . . ."*

Again she was shakily trying to push back the mat of damp hair from her forehead; Owen found himself doing it for her, mesmerized by the luminous softness in her eyes. His touch was soothing, gentling. Suddenly, neither of them was aware of the rain. "We'll get your baby to a doctor," he promised quietly.

The look of haunted tension faded from her expression; she almost smiled. "I wouldn't ask you, but my car won't run—"

Owen glanced at the growing confusion around them. Other cars were backing up, people clustering close, the police approaching. He turned back to her. "First things first—let's get you out of the rain. You can use my car."

"I'm *not* leaving Mari."

"I wasn't suggesting you leave your Mari. I'll bring you the baby."

"Wait. I'll get her myself. I don't want her to get wet in this rain."

"I'll see that she doesn't get wet."

"She's crying..."

"And you're getting soaked. Now, *in*." He held the car door open with one hand, propelled her forward with the other, and then hesitated. "What's your name?"

"Laura. Laura Anderson."

"Well, Laura Anderson, there are some clean shirts in back. Get yourself dry."

The door closed before Laura could say anything else. His car had the smell of expensive leather and the faint lingering scent of the man, both alien to the female and baby scents she'd been surrounded by in recent weeks. Feeling disoriented, she reached for one of his freshly laundered shirts to dry her face and hair, then twisted her head to see out the back window.

Outside, a man in a bright yellow slicker was

routing traffic around their cars. A charcoal sky was still dumping buckets of rain as a patrol car pulled up behind her crumpled Pinto. She saw it all in fleeting images; her eyes were fixed on the tall, dark-haired man bending over the front seat of her car.

Wrapping her arms around her chest, she closed her eyes and fought to regain emotional control. She'd never felt quite so close to hysteria before. However minor the accident, the crash was the last straw after months filled with crises. *Admit it, Laura. For once, it feels darn good to let someone else take charge, just for a few minutes . . .*

Her eyes flicked open. He was striding toward her, looking rather amusing, actually, with a diaper bag slung over his impeccably tailored suit. Except that she didn't see Mari. Alarmed, Laura reached for the door handle just as he opened the other side. Seeing the fluff of Mari's blond hair nestled between his shirt and suit coat, she breathed a quick sigh.

"What on earth did you do to make her stop crying?" She instantly extended her arms to the little one, only by accident letting her eyes travel up to his. Humor was glinting in his dark silver eyes, and his mouth was twisted in a peculiar expression.

"When I looked inside the car, I was half expecting to find an infant in desperate need of a hospital." He cleared his throat. "Not that I'm doubting your judgment, but are you *sure* she needs a doctor?"

Laura's arms folded protectively around the baby. "I know she *looks* healthy—"

"Thriving, healthy, pink-cheeked, and sassy."

"But she cries. If you'd heard her this morning..."

"Yes." He added politely, "Do you always dress her for arctic conditions?"

Laura's jaw dropped. "It was *raining* outside!"

"It's still sixty-five degrees. You had a thick blanket under her, another one over her, this *thing* completely covering her—"

"She's only three weeks old," Laura protested. "And the infant seat is too hard without a blanket. And this *thing* is a bunny suit that covers her head; you're supposed to keep a newborn's ears covered. They get ear infections. You have to be very careful—"

"The Spock from 'Star Trek' never worried about ear infections, and think of *his* ears," Owen murmured.

"Pardon?"

"Nothing. She's your first baby, isn't she?" He sighed. "Which suddenly explains a great deal."

"Now, what's that supposed to mean?" But her voice softened. Mari was trying to jam a tiny fist into her mouth, but she wasn't crying. Laura forgot the accident; she forgot the argument. The weight of the baby felt perfect in her arms, making up for just about everything that ever had or ever could happen to her.

When she glanced up again, the man was studying her with a faint smile. How amazing that at first she'd thought his mouth was rigid, his features uncompromisingly stern. His smile didn't erase the lines of authority and control, but there was definitely a kind man behind the threatening mask. Never one to trust a stranger, Laura abruptly realized that she already had, in allowing him to touch Mari. The thought was unsettling.

"I don't want to contradict the advice in your baby books, but do you think there's a slim chance she's hungry?" he asked tactfully.

"There's a good chance she's hungry," Laura agreed dismally. "She's always hungry. But she was also crying earlier, before she could possibly have been hungry."

"Hmm." Owen tried again. "She looks fat as a butterball."

"Too fat?" Laura said with alarm, and peeked at Mari's double chin.

"Not *too* fat. I was just trying to suggest that perhaps you don't need to worry quite so much about anything being terribly wrong with her."

"Well . . ." Belatedly, it occurred to Laura that she must be pretty desperate for reassurance, to take it from a man who looked as though he'd be more at home between satin sheets than changing diapers.

"In the meantime, there are two officers outside who need insurance and registration information . . ."

"I'll get it. I—" Thin wails started the moment Laura reached for her wallet. Her hand jerked back from her purse. "Oh, Mari . . ."

With a sigh, Owen took the bag from her and started rifling through brushes, combs, diapers, pins. He held up the well-thumbed *Mother's Almanac* with a skeptical look and finally surfaced with her wallet. "I'll get your license. Your registration in here, too?"

She looked blank.

"Skip it. I'll find it. Look, just feed your baby. I'll take care of the rest."

A pale pink glow streaked across her cheeks. "I can't feed her here."

Briskly, he tugged a dry shirt from his pile of clean laundry and handed it to her. "I understand. I figured you'd want a bottle from the diaper bag, and when there wasn't one, I realized that you were breast-feeding her. Just use the shirt to cover yourself. I won't let anyone near the car."

He was gone again. Through the back window, she could see him striding toward the policemen, but abruptly Mari's shrieks climbed into the next octave. Draping his shirt over her, she groped underneath for the tiny pearl buttons of her blouse. "Just a minute. Just a minute, darling. Please, Mari..."

There hadn't been time to buy nursing bras, but she wore the kind that fastened in front—just as easy to manage, when her fingers were steady enough. It took three tries, and then she winced when Mari clamped down on her nipple. A familiar taut ache filled her breasts, and she closed her eyes.

Only it didn't work. The baby's mouth opened, and Mari let out a furious wail. Laura coaxed her back; the baby pushed away. After several minutes, Laura gave up trying and simply rocked the frantic baby back and forth, back and forth. Stay calm, the books on nursing said. Sure. After an accident? Maybe she didn't have any milk. Maybe she'd run out. Good Lord, could it conceivably turn sour after only three hours?

When the car door swung open, Laura jumped, startled. "You're finished with the police already?" she tried to say calmly over the baby's screams.

"No, we're not done, but I could hear the baby crying from out there. Listen..." Owen leaned in, deliberately looking into Laura's eyes and no lower. "I know you're going to misunderstand this, but I've been around a ton of babies. I grew up with six younger brothers and sisters—and my sisters are having babies of their own now. They all breast-feed their infants, and my sister-in-law, Paige—"

"What the *hell* do you think you're doing?"

His palm was sliding gently between his shirt and her blouse. "Paige and Gary have three small ones. Gary's always talking about breast-feeding. Now, just take it easy..."

"Stop that!" Desperately, Laura tried to hold the baby, climb away from him, keep herself covered, and for godsake look unconcerned. Unfortunately, she ran out of places to back up. Warm, smooth fingers stroked her firm, supple breast with the touch of a lover.

Heat spread through her lower body in a rush. The sexual voltage was more potent than the slash of lightning outside. All the air left her lungs in a horrified whoosh.

"If you'll bring the baby close now..."

"There's no point. I haven't any—" The blend

of shock and despair in her voice hushed abruptly. Mari's piercing shrieks ceased as milk spurted into the infant's mouth.

Total silence instantly filled the car. A hectic color flooded Laura's face. "I . . . er . . . you can take your hand off my . . . um . . ."

Owen's palm lingered seconds longer before sliding away. His face averted, he protectively covered her once more with his shirt, his movements suddenly awkward. Owen couldn't remember having felt awkward in years. But one didn't bother with social conventions when there was trouble, he told himself; one acted. Being Owen, he could not have continued to stand there doing nothing while the baby cried and the mother grew more and more frantic with worry. Only . . . he'd hardly expected his own body's instantaneous reaction to the touch of her. He straightened. "Look. I'm sorry. That was way out of line—"

"Yes."

"In fact, I don't believe I just did that."

"Neither," Laura remarked, "do I."

"Owen's the name, by the way." He thought if he introduced himself he might seem less like a stranger to her. When her expression didn't change, he cleared his throat. "You see, ever since I was knee-high, there was always a baby in the family. My mother and sisters talk about nursing as easily as they talk about politics. I learned years ago that if a mother's tense, sometimes the milk won't come down. And my brother—"

"Yes. You told me."

"Would I be better off if I shut up?"

"Yes."

"I can't tell you how happy I would be to drop the subject. As long as you understand that I wasn't ... assaulting you."

He caught the first glimmer of humor in her eyes, a spark that erased the weariness from her cameo features. Even damp and disheveled, she had a special claim to natural loveliness. Owen caught his breath.

Laura had already caught hers. Now that Mari wasn't crying and his hand was back where it belonged, it occurred to her how foolish she was to have panicked. The man was hardly going to make a pass at her in front of the police and a crowd. He would hardly have made a pass, anyway, at a waif with straggly hair and no makeup and postpartum Jell-O for a stomach. "For heaven's sake, I didn't think you were."

Well, that was more than he was sure of. He studied her soft profile, the tangled mass of light brown hair, the sweep of bared white throat ... and reminded himself that babies weren't made by magic. Which meant she had a husband.

"I'll be back in a few minutes."

"Yes," Laura said politely. She couldn't wait to be rid of him.

"I should have asked you before if you wanted me to call anyone ..."

"No, but thank you." Laura stared with fascination at the windshield, aware that his eyes were suddenly riveted on her face.

Eventually, Owen closed the door again. By the time he'd finished with the police, the rain had quieted to a lazy drizzle. His mind wasn't on accident reports or insurance. It was on a fragile-looking woman with a brand-new baby who'd said she had no one to call.

A woman who'd wrecked his vintage Austin-Healey.

- 2 -

"THIS REALLY ISN'T necessary, you know."

"I know."

"I'd have appreciated a ride to the nearest phone, but the police would have done that much for me. And I never meant for you to get dragged in this far..."

"Laura," Owen said flatly. "I said I would get you and the baby to a doctor, and I will."

Laura fell silent, and then ventured again, "Look, I know how crazy I must have seemed. Hysterical woman, new mother, stranded, raving. I'd really like to correct that first impression. Would you believe that I was labeled 'Most Stable and Calm' in my high school yearbook?"

19

"I never heard of that category in high school yearbooks."

"Neither have I," she said dryly, then changed the subject. "I'm trying to let you off the hook. I'm sure you had a dozen things planned for the afternoon other than chauffeuring two strangers to their pediatrician."

True. Particularly when the pink-cheeked, happily sleeping infant on her shoulder couldn't possibly need a doctor—but Laura, Owen was discovering, was a stubborn woman. Also, she was determined to let him know that a man wasn't welcome in her life.

"And another thing . . ." Laura said quietly.

At a red light, Owen turned to study her, having no interest in hearing yet "another thing." She was sitting as close to the door as possible and wearing a smile like a shield. What the hell did she think he was going to do, attack her?

Actually, that was partly the cause of his headache. He wanted to. Not attack her, exactly, but definitely touch. The impulse was embarrassing, and offended every grain of integrity Owen possessed. He was hardly in the habit of picking up married women, much less young mothers with their offspring in tow. Laura had clearly recovered from the accident; the color was back in her face and her voice was calm. He didn't have the slightest excuse for continuing to hang around.

Except that every instinct told him something was wrong. She shouldn't be alone, not this soon after having a baby, with no one to call. He was concerned about the circles under her eyes, and she ought to be several pounds heavier . . . and her coral mouth was as naturally kissable as any he'd seen in thirty-three years. *Where* was her husband?

"And another thing," Laura repeated. "I have good insurance coverage. It'll pay for the repairs to your car. And if there's anything that isn't covered, I promise you I'll take care of it."

"Yes." He looked straight ahead. Insurance was the last thing on his mind, but it gave him an opening. "Would you prefer I call your husband if there's any problem?"

"That won't be necessary. The policy's in my name."

Which answered nothing. The woman's quiet-voiced replies were gradually reducing him to insanity. He was left with little choice but to be straightforward and blunt. "If *I* were your husband, I would want to *know* you'd been in an accident."

Those turquoise eyes flickered briefly over his face. Her cucumber-cool smile didn't falter. "I'm not married—actually, my divorce was final a month ago. Is that what you've been trying to ask?"

It wasn't pleasant, having his own straightforward and blunt manner turned back on him. "Yes."

At his disgruntled expression, Laura chuckled. "Relax, I didn't think you were prying. You were just being kind. Thank you," she added warmly as he parked in front of the doctor's office. "I'll take a taxi home."

"I'll see you in."

"There's no need."

The woman could give lessons on destroying a man's ego, but he took her inside anyway.

In the waiting room, Owen collapsed in a chair and tried to figure out what on earth he thought he was doing there. He had plenty to do this afternoon besides sit in a roomful of toddlers. The only reading material was on childrearing, breastfeeding, and potty-training. The six women in the room kept looking at him, and he felt distinctly out of place. Shifting, he glanced at his watch.

She'd been in with the doctor for two minutes. Already it seemed like two hours.

After a quick trip to the car, he settled down with *Forbes*. A detailed article charted the previous year's patterns in commodities and predicted heavy bidding in cocoa futures, which would affect chocolate prices over the next six months. Chocolate was Owen's livelihood; he could have been engrossed, if a sticky-handed one-year-old hadn't used his pant leg to pull himself up and then stand there, wiggle-bottomed, asking, "Da? *Da?*"

The boy's mother rushed over, all blushes and flushes, to grab the urchin. Owen heard a brunette whispering to her neighbor about how her sex life had ceased after the baby was born. He sighed, raising his *Forbes* to eye level.

He was pacing by the window a half-hour later, wondering exactly what would make a beautiful woman with turquoise eyes seek a divorce in the middle of a pregnancy, when he heard a low, throaty chuckle. Laura was standing at the receptionist's desk, juggling the baby, her purse, the diaper bag, and a checkbook. The lines of strain and tension had disappeared from her face. Her smile was radiant, and a sassy brightness lit her eyes. She radiated vibrancy.

Suddenly, he knew exactly why he'd waited for her.

Tucking the magazine under his arm, he strode toward her. When she turned, that smile encompassed him. Or he wanted it to. "The baby passed her checkup?"

"With flying colors!"

He tried to look surprised. Reaching for her bag, he asked, "What did the doctor say?"

Her smile suddenly wavered. "I just realized—you really didn't have to wait for me."

"Forget it. It'll only take a few minutes to get you home."

As they walked out to his car, Owen could barely keep from chuckling. Laura's expression was rueful. "He claims Mari's the healthiest baby he's seen in ages."

"And—"

"And he told me to quit worrying."

"And—"

"And," she related dryly, "he told me to stop reading baby books, let the baby cry occasionally, and drink a glass of wine every afternoon." She settled into his car and announced, "I am *not* going to let Mari cry, and I'm definitely not going to drink wine while I'm nursing her."

Owen hid a grin. "I'm certainly glad we came all this way to get the doctor's advice."

"He also told me to try to wait a whole week before I come back again. Owen, you can quit trying to look deadpan. It's perfectly all right to laugh at me. *I* laugh at me. Maybe I wouldn't overreact quite so much if I knew something about babies . . . but I don't." Her eyes softened as she stroked the baby's cheek. "And Mari's everything to me. She's all I have."

Owen's hands suddenly tightened on the steering wheel. Her tone was light, the statement simple, but he heard pain from somewhere, an ocean of it. He studied her quietly as they drove. At first glance, she was simply a young woman holding a baby, surrounded by diaper bags and purse and blankets.

There was more to Laura than a first glance revealed, though. The fierce love she had for her child, the mask of control she wore over those fragile features, the emotional shadows he saw in her eyes. When she caught him studying her, he smiled. Lord, she was beautiful.

Laura smiled back. Owen—he hadn't told her his last name—was making her damn nervous. An hour ago, she'd definitely needed a hero; she'd been a basket case. But no more. Surely he could see she was fine now?

Imposing on him went utterly against the grain. Pushing herself on any man went utterly against the grain. She'd done that once, for the space of a three-year marriage. Once, she might have believed that nothing could dent her faith in herself as a woman. Peter had, in the space of five minutes. Irrevocably.

"Laura? What's wrong?"

"Nothing." She stared at the tree-lined streets of Ridgefield. "Absolutely nothing, now."

Although New York was only an hour away, there was no hint of the bustling metropolis here. Restored eighteenth-century homes were nestled amid trees and leafy privacy; roads curled through hills and valleys. Laura could feel Owen's eyes on her as he turned up the steep drive to her beautiful place, and she felt a rush of pride. Now *you can see. I was never a waif, Buster, just a lady in temporary trouble.*

This was hers, all hers and Mari's. At the top of the hill, surrounded by woods, stood a Cape Cod–style cottage. Behind it, wood hyacinths rambled down a ravine to a splashing silvery creek below. The grass in front of the house was a tiny bit overgrown, and there were still packing crates on the porch, but a woman fresh out of the hospital could only do so much, and Mr. Sexy Businessman could clearly see she owned a terrific piece of property.

"You just moved in?" he asked casually as she climbed out of the car, carrying Mari.

"Yes. I—"

"Alone? Right when you were having the baby?"

She sighed. She wished he had looked at the ravine instead of at the packing crates. "It *was* awkward timing, but I couldn't move out of New York until the divorce was final. Even then, I would have had enough time to get settled—if Mari hadn't arrived early."

"Laura?"

"Hmmm?" She was covering Mari's head with a

blanket. The rain had stopped, but the late afternoon was cool and damp.

"You have family close by?"

"Just Mom and Dad."

"So where *is* your mother?"

She blinked. "In India. Where the devil is yours?"

He chuckled, a disarming chuckle. If Laura had been the least bit inclined to be attracted to a man because of his warm laughter and changeable gray-silver eyes and winsome smile . . . but she wasn't. What Peter hadn't destroyed in the way of sexual feelings, giving birth certainly had. Labor could make a rabbit think twice about ever wanting sex again.

"I only asked because it seemed logical your mother would come to help you. My mother stayed with all of my sisters for a few weeks after each of their babies arrived."

"Well, my mother doesn't approve of daughters divorcing their husbands in the middle of pregnancies. When she and Dad booked a trip around the world, I was supposed to 'come around' and turn to Peter if she wasn't there."

"But you didn't. You went through the birth alone." He looked ready to hit someone.

He'd reached the door ahead of her, and she sighed, shifting Mari in her arms. "I take it you're coming in?"

"The doctor ordered you to drink a glass of wine just about this time of day."

"I don't have any wine."

He motioned to a paper bag buried behind her

diaper bag in his arms. "I do. Picked some up this morning. Might as well share it."

As if accidentally, his eyes wandered to the smashed rear end of his car, and Laura felt a rush of guilt. She'd been nothing but trouble to him all afternoon, and now she was being churlish as well. "Come in," she invited hesitantly, and immediately noted the triumphant gleam in his eyes.

"Let me take the baby for you."

"You don't have to do that. Actually, no one's held Mari but me, and I—"

He stole the child so swiftly that she found herself standing awkwardly, feeling exposed somehow. His eyes took a determinedly slow path, from her high-necked lace blouse over her ripe, firm breasts, down to slender bare legs and sandals. She felt a rush of the uglies. Her stomach wasn't quite flat yet; her breasts seemed disproportionately big from nursing; her legs were too slender these days. Not that it mattered what he thought, but the flush she felt climbing her cheeks was a surprise. Perhaps she still had some feminine vanity left, even after Peter.

Owen's eyes met hers, opaque, unreadable, but there was something ... dangerous there. Something she'd never expected. And then it was gone. He turned, setting down the diaper bag, and studied the room.

"You like antiques?"

"They're my business." Again, pride echoed in her voice. At first look, the room was a jumble of baby gear and packing crates. Beneath that, though, the place was ideal for the two of them. Upstairs, a roomy loft with a slanted roof had been divided into two bedrooms and a bath. The main floor contained an old-fashioned country kitchen, a dining room she could use as an office, and the long living room they were standing in now.

Plank paneling and casement windows and a huge fieldstone fireplace set off her treasures . . . the bonnet-topped highboy, the comb-back Windsor chairs, the oak refectory table with baluster legs, the Georgian burred desk. The couch was Jenny Lind—a criminal transgression for a period antique fanatic, but Laura had opted for comfort; its blue and white cushions were thick and comfortable, matching the crisp curtains. A lighthouse clock stood on the mantel, and the bookshelves were already filled with books on the eighteenth-century antiques that were her stock in trade.

"You sell antiques?"

"Actually, my business is finding them." Laura moved forward swiftly, self-consciously straightening things. "My ex-husband was a musician—a cellist—and we traveled around from city to city. That gave me a chance to scour the countryside, comparing prices and quality, finding all the best sources." *Stop babbling, Laura.* "Anyway, I act as a middleman. For example, if a store has a customer looking for a step-down Windsor settee, or a baroque chimney piece, or an English linen press, they call me and I track it down. Good eighteenth-century antiques are hard to find; they're usually hidden away on estates. I'll have to go back to traveling in time, but for these first months with Mari, I've arranged to do most of my searching on the phone. Owen?"

"So you're trying to work, as well as move in and care for a new baby." No surprise echoed in his wry tone, but a rare twist of jealousy gnawed in Owen's head. So the guy had been artistic, a musician. Owen could claim courage, guts, and sound survival instincts in the corporate jungle, but not a single artistic bone. So if that appealed to her in a man... And he'd expected her to talk about her ex-husband with anger, or pain, or *something* to indicate the reason for a fast divorce in the middle of a pregnancy. But Laura mentioned Peter as casually as she might discuss chicken soup.

"Owen?" A frantic note had crept into her voice.

"Yes?"

He'd taken off his coat, and the baby was perched face-down under his arm. Laura said politely, "You're holding Mari as if she were a football."

He glanced down. "I haven't found a baby yet who doesn't like being held like a football." He paused. "Where's your corkscrew?"

She hadn't the slightest idea, but finding it at least gave her something to do with her hands. Owen trailed her to the kitchen, peeking into the freezer and refrigerator.

"Do you really have six brothers and sisters?"

"Yes. Spread out all over the country these days, except for Gary—I think I mentioned him—and a sister, Susan. They both live nearby. I think my parents intended to have only one child... I was seven before they went on a one-a-year binge." He lifted a package from her freezer. "The youngest finally reached twenty this year, and the confusion at family gatherings seems to get worse every year. Most of them are married and have kids of their own."

"Hmmm." She couldn't find the corkscrew anywhere. Funny, that. Normally she could lay her hands on anything in the kitchen. The room was a joy, with hanging pots and fresh greenery and an old-fashioned raised hearth big enough to cook in. She had hung the Dresden blue curtains yesterday, and a splash of white hyacinths now sat in the center of the oak table. There was ample space for everything . . . except that a broad-shouldered, dark-haired man seemed to be everywhere.

"You have fresh asparagus," he commented.

She heard him but deliberately didn't answer. She watched her baby, ready to pounce whenever Mari let out the first scream. Mari hadn't been this good since she'd been born.

"A couple of chicken breasts, marinated and broiled? Does that sound good for dinner?'

Laura brandished the corkscrew and flashed a brilliant smile. "I *knew* I had one, but I haven't had anything alcoholic in so long . . ." She could hardly wait to hand him the bottle. He'd *have* to give Mari back while he uncorked it; no one could do that with only one hand . . . but he managed, flipping Mari over his shoulder like a sack of potatoes. The baby gurgled, oblivious of her mother's look of horror.

"Wineglasses?"

She found one for him. He reached into the cupboard and took down a second glass, filled both, wandered to the window with the baby, and stared out at his bashed-in car.

Laura sighed mentally. "Would you like to stay for dinner?"

"Thank you, yes."

Whether he knew it or not, she thought darkly, she wasn't letting him manipulate her, bashed-in car or no. For keeping Mari happy, she would have given him fortunes. Dinner was cheaper.

An hour later, Laura peeked nervously under the kitchen table. Mari was settled in the triangle of Owen's crossed knee.

"Laura. She's *fine.*"

"I don't understand it. She's not crying. She *always* cries when I try to eat dinner." Laura's face peeked over the edge of the table. "Did I tell you that dinner was delicious?"

"Four times."

"How did a bachelor from a large family learn to cook like that?"

He chuckled. "Learning to cook was a matter of survival, not choice. I still haven't mastered the art of following a recipe."

He'd mastered a few other things, though, she thought idly. A stranger shouldn't be sitting at her kitchen table, and yet he was. She'd never meant to drink the glass of wine, and yet she had. Owen had the gift of making odd things seem natural. He'd kept her laughing through dinner with stories

of his large, unruly family. He also had wonderful
dancing eyes, the most seductive tenor she'd ever
heard, and an easy way of making himself at home.
Laura, what is this man doing in your house?

"Owen, what *are* you doing here?" she asked
determinedly.

He raised a dark eyebrow quizzically.

"Saving a stranded woman. Chauffeuring her
around. Cooking her dinner. You make a habit of
this?"

"I've been exiled from my own family," he said
gravely.

"Exiled?"

"It's difficult to explain. You see, chocolates are
the family business—did I tell you Reesling is my
last name? And for the last seven—"

"Reesling? Reesling Chocolates?"

For an instant, he couldn't stop looking at her.
Sheer lust filled her eyes, vivid and uninhibited.
She had let her guard down for those few seconds.
Mischief sparkled from her. And if he'd had the
least idea that chocolates were her nemesis, he'd
have brought up the subject an hour before.

"My dad used to buy them for special occasions,"
Laura confessed. "Thirty dollars a pound, all
wrapped in satin boxes, those beautiful little
shapes . . ." Abruptly, she came back to earth. "Wait
a minute. Let's get back to why you're 'exiled' from
your family."

He would have preferred to talk chocolates. In
her bedroom.

He settled for answering a gentle stream of questions and watching her eyes change from the blue-green of the sea to the turquoise of the gem. She had a most disturbing habit of . . . listening.

And he had a long-standing policy of not talking about himself, but she coaxed the family history from him. For the last seven years, he'd run the business single-handed, while his dad retired and his younger siblings were busy getting educated— and married. The Reeslings owned cacao plantations in Brazil, transported the beans to New York, and manufactured chocolates from their own secret recipes. Like most of the good chocolate firms worldwide, Reesling's wasn't a massive corporation, but it was a complex international business. Running it, Owen had discovered, was both satisfying and challenging, particularly since he had been determined to double production.

"Which you've done." Laura had no doubts.

"Which I've done," he agreed. And he'd turned into a workaholic in the process. Of his six brothers and sisters, only Gary and Susan were interested in the business. Both were well educated and skilled in managing the business, and they had been indispensable to him. "Only, according to them, I've turned into a domineering, autocratic tyrant," he explained to Laura glumly.

"Have you?"

"Hell, yes."

She chuckled, but her smile was compassionate. "There's more to it than that, though, isn't there, Owen?"

He nodded. "Family businesses don't work un-

less each member is willing to sink or swim alone.
Any firm that takes on all of Uncle Johnny's forty-
seven nephews out of family loyalty is going to go
down the tubes unless each is prepared to pull his
weight. And I have two siblings who are dying to
pull their weight. Gary's got good marketing ideas;
Susan has a degree in chemistry and wants to try a
dozen new products. Neither of them wants the top
chair, just a chance to try out their management
wings. And that just wasn't happening..."

"Because you couldn't let go of the controls,"
Laura guessed quietly.

"I told you I was a tyrant." He shook his head.
"I pulled the plug for about six months—not totally,
but I'm trying to stay away unless they actually ask
for help. They've got an experienced staff behind
them, but they need time and freedom, without me
constantly telling them what to do. They need their
chance—and, frankly, I need to change. Anyway,
enough of talking about myself."

The baby let out a sharp, piercing wail, and Owen
gently handed her to Laura. "I'm afraid the princess
just ran out of patience."

"Owen..." She wanted to say something reas-
suring but wasn't sure how. In spite of his dry humor, Laura guessed he'd never meant to share a
personal crisis. Still, he was a relative stranger and
she didn't have the right to reassure him. He'd labeled himself a domineering workaholic, but dom-
inating wasn't the same thing as domineering. He
was a man who naturally took control, but he didn't
seem to lose any of his humanity in the process. If

he saw himself as a tyrant, Laura didn't. To her he'd shown caring and compassion for her baby, and she didn't like to see him being so hard on himself.

She wanted to say something, but in a minute her arms closed around the pink-wrapped bundle, and her attention was distracted. Softness glowed on her features. Mari was her world. For an instant, she'd been so immersed in Owen's story that she'd almost forgotten that. Impossible. The baby was her life.

"I'll clear the table while you nurse the baby. And it's cooled down so much I'll lay a small fire— if you had the chimney checked out before you moved in?"

"I . . . yes, and there's even a little wood on the back porch, but you don't have to do—" Mari let out another furious wail, and Laura looked at Owen nervously. All right, so he wasn't quite a stranger anymore. Maybe she'd even enjoyed the last few hours, and maybe she even felt unwillingly drawn to a man who'd shouldered heavy responsibilities for too long. Still, the bottom line was that no man belonged in her living room.

His eyes met hers. "If you'd just turn your chair around," he suggested gently. "Laura, I won't intrude on your privacy."

She flushed; he knew she was embarrassed to nurse in front of him. Paying no attention to her, he brought in an armful of twigs and knelt by the hearth, stacking them together with a few small logs. By the time he flicked the match, she had turned the chair around and bent her head away from him.

He moved toward the kitchen, shifting plates to the counter, a faint smile on his mouth as he watched her. The fire was little more than ribbons of flame, its amber glow dancing in her hair. He heard her murmur softly to the baby, saw her fumble with her blouse buttons. The infant wailed, then fell silent. Laura's face was only a fire-warmed shadow against the paneling, but he saw the sudden wince when the baby latched on, then the sensually radiant smile as she leaned her head back.

He envied the baby.

After he had disposed of the dishes, his eyes narrowed on the space around him. The clutter of packing boxes bothered him; her half-empty refrigerator bothered him. Laura clearly had too much on her plate.

Financially, she was obviously solvent. Her property was expensive; the baby gear was the finest quality; her antiques were worth a small fortune. She was just so . . . alone.

And Laura was a woman who shouldn't be alone, if any man had sense in his head. She was proud and warm and intelligent; her eyes had a sensual incandescence when she looked at her little one. Such a great capacity for love.

Why was she alone? What kind of fool had her ex-husband been?

Carrying his glass of wine, he returned to the fire and crouched down to add another log. Orange sparks flew up the chimney, hot and crackling. He sensed that she'd quickly drawn up the baby blanket to cover herself. There was no need; he wasn't looking.

He didn't need to look. In his mind he carried an indelible picture of her bared breast bathed in the warmth of the fire's glow. He settled on her couch and sipped the wine, seeing images he had no business seeing ... and willing them anyway.

Laura shifted the baby to the other breast. "Owen? You live in Ridgefield?"

"I bought a house here about three years ago. Truthfully, though, I haven't spent more than a few months in it in all that time. It needs some work ..." He swirled the golden liquid in his glass. His house was the last thing on his mind. For once, even the business wasn't on his mind. His conscience was reading him a riot act. Licentious thoughts were inappropriate around a woman fresh out of the hospital, but his mind wouldn't stop filling up with ... images.

When Laura shifted the baby to her other breast, he knew that the flame would cast amber and shadow on her supple skin.

"Owen?"

He saw the shadow of the baby's fist flailing, then curling possessively on her mother's breast. He gulped the last of his wine and fumbled for the track of conversation. She'd asked something about why they grew the cocoa beans in Brazil. "Most beans are grown in either West Africa or Brazil. Soil and climate affect their taste. A blend of Brazilian beans produces the sharpest, clearest flavor ... though I doubt you'd get our competition to agree."

He hoped that answered her question, because he'd already forgotten it. She propped the baby on her shoulder to burp. For an instant, her bare breast was silhouetted in the shadow of the fire.

Owen felt abruptly more rational when she finished buttoning up her blouse. At least until she turned around, and he saw the natural, sensual sweetness of her face.

The baby was sleeping on her shoulder, very full and contented. Owen felt hollow and frustrated, and could only hope he didn't look that way.

Laura stood up. "I'm going to lay her down," she whispered.

When she took the baby upstairs, Owen rolled down his shirtsleeves, buttoned the cuffs, and glanced around for his suit jacket. He wasn't staying; he refused to allow himself to stay. She was exhausted and needed rest. But the first thing he said to her when she came back down was "Would you come outside with me for a few minutes?"

- 3 -

"JUST FOR A few minutes," Owen promised her.

Laura glanced uncertainly up the loft stairs. "I can't leave Mari."

"We won't go far. You'll be able to hear her."

Laura stepped outside ahead of him, her arms folded tightly under her chest. Her kitchen door led to a cedar deck overlooking the ravine.

The night was cool. A faint breeze murmured through the new summer leaves. In the distance, she could hear the gurgling rush of the creek, and all around her the rain had intensified all the smells of early summer—grass and pungent earth and the sweet hyacinths.

Behind her, Owen leaned against the cedar rail.

She could feel his eyes on her, and when she turned, the breeze tossed a wisp of pale hair across her cheek; she brushed it away. Moonlight touched his features, the lines of strength and purpose, the opaque shine of his eyes. Away from the firelit room, away from Mari, alone with him in the darkness, she suddenly felt aware of him as a man.

Her tongue was inexplicably tripping itself, trying to find something to say. "I love this place," she said lightly. "All the time I was growing up, I loved traveling and never really missed having a home. But since Mari..."

"You picked a beautiful site. Come here, Laura."

She smiled, a cool, bright smile that denied the strange little shiver that raced up her spine. *Come here, Laura.* That was all he'd said. Nothing... dangerous.

"It probably would have been more practical simply to find another apartment in New York, but..." She saw his hand reach out to her in the darkness, and smiled brilliantly again. "I wanted a home. Something of my own. My grandmother set up a trust for me, so I could afford it. Between that money and the fees I earn from my work—"

His hand closed on hers, pulled her inexorably closer. She suddenly couldn't remember what she'd been talking about. He looked down at her for a long moment, and then simply wrapped his arms around her. He smelled like the wine, like wind. Laura stiffened, feeling awkward and strange and ...helpless. Human contact could be so terribly comforting. A hug. The warmth of arms around her. She'd been alone for months now, and afraid of so many things.

His heart ticked with the steadiness of a clock in the darkness. His white shirt was soft against her cheek. The warmth of his body protected her from the night's chill. "Lord, you feel good," he murmured.

Long, firm fingers stole under her hair, and his thumb soothingly rubbed the tense cord of the nape of her neck. Where an overt pass would have freed her to move away, his gentle touch hypnotized, disarmed. "We've both been alone," he whispered. "I don't mean away from people, I just mean . . . alone. Temporarily uprooted, changing our lives . . . I know what it feels like, Laura."

She tilted her head back. Her skin was so soft, her eyes so luminous. Owen sensed her wariness, and summoned thirty-three years of willpower to keep from kissing those delicately curled lips . . . but lost. His mouth hovered, then blocked the streak of silver moonlight on her face. Cool and smooth, his lips covered hers lightly. A kiss of softness, of hello, of simple sharing.

Slow and shy, her hands gradually moved to his waist, seeking something to hold on to. *Laura, don't be a fool*. She heard the voice and ignored it. Owen was warmth and strength; this was just a lost moment in time; and as long as she felt nothing sexual . . . it was all right. Surely there was nothing so terrible in needing to be held?

His lips strayed from her mouth to her cheek, into her hair. The wind died; the rustle of leaves stilled above their heads. The hush was sudden and soft and... alluring. The tips of her breasts just grazed his chest; her skirt brushed his thighs, teasing her into awareness. Then his lips pressed against hers again, this time not quite so gently. This time he deliberately made her aware of the shape of his mouth, the taste of him, the coaxing seductive power of a man who knew how to kiss.

Once, she had, too. Once, she'd blithely invited kisses, the primal tease and parry of tongues. Once, she'd believed herself a vibrantly sexual woman, relieved to be married, so she could unashamedly express that secret well of sensuality without fear.

She knew better now. She knew better than to relinquish an ounce of control over her emotions; it was easier to feel nothing. But Owen... his lips kept rubbing over hers, coaxing a response she knew wasn't there. She didn't want it there, yet her heart was suddenly pounding, an ache welling up inside her that was impossibly huge and thick and painful...

She was no child, no virgin anymore. She knew what he wanted. His mouth was hungry, lonely, reminding her that nights alone could be endless. Her hands climbed his arms, tightly clutched his shoulders, and suddenly she was wildly kissing him back. Trembling lips sought the security of his, possession by his. Anything that would make that terrible ache go away.

Owen's tongue drove deeper into the darkness of her mouth. So sweet, so warm... she was all abandoned fire in the black of night, a fierce flame, as bright as life, as woman. He'd sought only a simple kiss, but he needed more now. He needed Laura.

His hands slid in a rush down her spine, her sides, wanting to learn the touch of her, feeling the soft crush of lace where he wanted to feel skin. *Mine,* said his hands. The primal need to claim, to establish possession . . . every male instinct intuitively recognized this woman as different. Laura felt right in his arms as no other woman had felt right. Rationally, he knew it wasn't going too far, not here, not now. That didn't matter. It only mattered that she feel as he did, that this richness of touch was rare and sweet and special.

His palm strayed to her ribs; he heard her sudden intake of breath, savored it. His fingers stole higher, gently rounding on the firm, taut thrust of her breast.

Like a startled fawn, Laura stiffened, jerked back. The roar of a dozen memories filled her ears like the sound of an angry ocean's surf. Peter might as well have been looking over her shoulder. *"You're much too abandoned,"* he would have said. *"Do you have to go at it like a hellcat?"*

God, the shame. Heart pounding, Laura would have fled if Owen's hand hadn't swiftly, firmly closed over hers, forcing her to face him.

His eyes wouldn't leave her alone, searching her face. His touch, fiercely passionate moments before, was suddenly infinitely gentle, yet he wouldn't free her hand. He could feel her captured fingers trembling. "I didn't mean to frighten you," he said quietly.

"No. You didn't."

"Laura—"

She couldn't look at him.

His voice was barely a whisper. "What the hell did that man do to you?"

As if he knew she wouldn't answer, he released her hand. She might have imagined the brush of his fingers in her hair; his touch was that swift, that elusive. Seconds later, he was gone, the throaty purr of his engine the only sound in the night, and then even that was gone.

Don't come back, Laura thought fiercely. *Just . . . don't come back.*

Laura glanced at the clock as she laid the sleeping baby back in her crib. Five-thirty. The sun was just thinking about getting up; a faint lavender haze hovered in the treetops outside.

Mari usually slept after her last feeding; Laura never could. Yawning, she pulled a yellow crinkle blouse on over white pants. Barefoot in front of the mirror, she twisted her hair back and fastened it with a rubber band, then pinned it in a loose coil, out of her way. Her father used to say that the old-fashioned look suited her. Lace and cameos and antiques, she thought wryly; none of them were part of the twentieth century.

Before tiptoeing downstairs, she flicked a blanket and sheet over her bed. She had decorated Mari's room first; her own had not seemed important. The mattress and box springs were still on the floor. The William and Mary four-poster frame was leaning against the wall, waiting until Laura had the time—

and the strength—to put the bed together.

That could wait, but she *had* to find the energy today to unpack her files, make business calls, shop for food, do some laundry . . . Her mind buzzed with a dozen plans, until she passed the hall mirror and noted her own rueful expression. *You're willing to think about anything but Owen this morning, aren't you?*

He won't be back, she assured herself as she puttered around the kitchen, brewing coffee, watering her plants. She finished off a banana and a slice of melon before there was a knock on the door.

Owen's suit was pale blue with a gray stripe, very elegant, very subdued on his tall, lean frame, and his eyes hadn't changed from that unreadable gunmetal that had so disturbed her the night before.

"Good morning, Laura."

Just like melted butter, that voice. "Well, good morning!" The surprise in her voice was totally fake. She had known he'd be back. And for the first time since Mari was born, she desperately wished the baby would wake up, even if she cried. Laura didn't want to be alone with him.

"May I come in?"

As far as she could tell, he was already in.

"I knew you'd be up," Owen said easily. "I have to leave for the city in an hour, so I won't stay long. Mari sleeping?"

"Yes, but she'll be up any minute." *Mari, wake up.*

"I rented a car for you. It'll be here this morning. Your insurance money will come through in a day or two, but in the meantime you have to be able to get out."

"I . . . That was kind of you." She stood there, aware she was smiling foolishly. *We both know we talked about that yesterday. The thing is, Owen, yesterday I believed I could handle anything. I doubt you would even believe what I've handled this last year alone. But yesterday I also discovered that there's one part of my life I can't handle at all . . .*

"I brought coffee cake. And something else." He handed her a small, wrapped package, tied with a bright silk ribbon, marked unmistakably REESLING.

"Owen, for heaven's sake . . ."

"Just open it."

Inside was a white chocolate rose, its stem in dark chocolate, a very tiny, perfectly molded flower far too exquisite to eat.

"You said chocolates were your nemesis, didn't you?"

Laura looked up, confusion in her eyes.

"Relax," he said softly. "Six o'clock in the morning is no time to worry about anything."

She took a breath. "True," she murmured.

"I'm desperate for a cup of coffee."

She said swiftly, "As long as that's all you want."

His smile was dangerous, but he simply sat down and poured himself a cup of coffee. Laura groped for something to do with her hands, and came up with the brilliant idea of dragging a laundry basket up to the kitchen table and folding diapers. No man could get . . . ideas while watching a woman fold diapers.

To her shock, he watched her fold a few diapers

and then reached for a stack and began folding them himself.

Ten minutes later, she was transported five hundred years into the past, to the time when Montezuma, the Aztec emperor, considered chocolate so precious that a golden goblet was filled only once with a cocoa brew and then destroyed.

"Chocolate was used as currency by the Aztecs," Owen explained conversationally. "Around the time Cortez was exploring Mexico, a hundred cocoa beans would buy a slave. Being a greedy man, he figured he'd found a potential gold mine, so he took cocoa beans with him on the rest of his travels, planting them in Haiti and Trinidad and Bioko—"

"Bioko?" she questioned.

"An island near West Africa. Keep in mind that Europe hadn't even heard of cocoa or chocolate by the fifteen hundreds..."

She kept it in mind. Actually, she was trying to keep a lot of things in mind, but it was hard. Chocolates had been her weakness since she was six, and she couldn't quite bring herself to kick the man out when he was doing nothing more than idly talking about a subject that fascinated her. She poured him a second cup of coffee, then pushed the folded diapers aside and reached for a pile of size-newborn undershirts. As Owen continued to answer her steady battery of questions, the mound of unfolded laundry diminished and finally disappeared.

Owen immediately stood up, reached for his suit-jacket, and glanced at his watch. "I've got a train to catch this morning."

Laura couldn't prevent a small smile. "I thought

you were learning how to relax and stay away from work."

"I *am* relaxed. But cocoa futures dropped five points last night . . ." He hesitated, giving her a rueful look. "Some people can't learn patience all at once."

"No."

"And I'm only going to stop in the office for a minute. I'm not going to say a word, even if Gary's reorganized every marketing plan I've set up in the last five years."

"No?" Laura chuckled as she followed him outside. Sunshine caught in his hair, glinted in the dark strands, sparkled in his eyes when he turned to her. For a moment, she simply studied him, surprised at how much she liked the man. "Every instinct tells me you trained your brother and sister exceedingly well, long before you temporarily gave up the reins of control. And you said you had an experienced staff."

"True. I still can't stand it," he murmured. "I have to *see* that things are going well."

She laughed; he delighted in the sound and reluctantly moved toward the door. He was leaving—and not because of work, though he'd deliberately given her that impression. To stay any longer simply wasn't wise. It had taken an hour to erase the wariness in her eyes, an hour to make her comfortable enough to tease him.

His family kept telling him he needed to learn to play again, and he knew they were right. Business crises and challenges and competition had always been puzzle pieces on a board for Owen, the tougher the better. His mistake had been to make work his whole life, and it wasn't enough. Not anymore. He wanted and needed a private life.

And a woman. He'd had a variety of relationships over the years, and some of them had been good. None had filled that elusive niche, but perhaps that had been his own fault. It was too easy for him to take charge of a relationship, to keep the controls, and he'd always seemed to gravitate toward women who wanted just that from him. Strength, though, could be a double-edged sword. No man was always strong, and dammit, he had more faults than most.

He wanted a woman he could be honest with. Who could accept his faults as he tried to change and grow. A woman capable of total commitment, as he was; a woman who wasn't intimidated by the take-charge tendencies he knew he had to temper; a woman who was even a little too proud. He understood pride.

And the woman with turquoise eyes had already stirred his soul. "Laura? Did I tell you about the chemical composition of chocolates?"

"No." She cocked her head curiously, leaning over the cedar rail as he went down the steps.

"Chocolate has small amounts of a substance called phenylethylamine. Actually, that's a natural chemical that's also produced in the brain—under certain conditions."

"What conditions?"

"Reach down with your hand and I'll show you." With a quizzical frown, she did so. His fingers reached out and touched hers, tip to tip. No more. Just the pressure of the pads of their fingers, just the hold he established by eye-to-eye contact, just the heat that suddenly flowed between them, hotter than flame, more fragile than sunlight.

"That chemical naturally occurs," Owen gently informed her, "when two people are falling in love. Touch isn't even always required. It still happens. My chemist claims phenylethylamine is a natural aphrodisiac, if you believe in that kind of thing."

She jerked her hand back, her cheeks flushed. "I don't!"

"No?" He smiled, then turned and strode to his car.

"Owen!"

He didn't turn back.

"Owen, *don't*. You're *crazy*. I just had a baby; you know that!"

"Just nibble on that chocolate," he called out to her as he opened his car door. "I'll be back, Laura."

He was back the next morning, and the next, and the next. He didn't mention aphrodisiacs again, and he didn't touch her, but by Saturday the refrigerator contained a small mountain of delicate treats. A white chocolate unicorn, a milk chocolate tulip, a cameo in creamy white and darkest dark. He couldn't possibly understand what those small gifts did to her. Did a friend offer a drink to an alcoholic? A cigarette to a reformed smoker? Owen wasn't kind.

Laura served him coffee and mutinously folded diapers while he made himself at home. She made brilliant efforts at looking terrible. That wasn't hard. Finding time to comb her hair took miracles, between night feedings, day feedings, trying to run a business and at the same time give Mari her complete attention. If he really wanted simply to sit there and fold diapers and discuss the merits of pacifiers versus thumb-sucking, it was fine with her.

When he didn't show up on Saturday, she wasn't surprised. Sooner or later he had to realize there was no point in involving himself in her life. She made a pot of coffee and found herself staring out the window a dozen times, but she refused to admit she missed him. Laura was realistic. She didn't have anything to offer this man. Or any man.

It was just that the man seemed to have insinuated himself into her life so easily. He was someone she could talk to. Company. Someone who could make her laugh, who could put a sparkle in those mornings when a long day of chores stretched ahead of her, offering only endless monotony.

And it *did* turn into one of those days. Mari decided to wake up early, and was fitful and cranky all morning. The phone never stopped ringing. Bridgeman's had a customer who wanted a George III library staircase, Campbell preferably; could she find one? And an antique dealer wanted her to track down a Gothic Revival bird cage.

She knew of a library staircase in Indiana, and the bird cage she could find if she could spend an hour or two on the phone—but Mari kept crying.

By midafternoon, Laura gave up hope of both commissions, hope of having lunch, hope of finding a moment to brush her hair, and simply paced the living room with the baby, back and forth, back and forth. She had tried putting Mari in the infant seat, the swing, the playpen, the crib. Each produced furious wails.

Humming lullabies, Laura carried the baby on her shoulder, walking in a pattern around the comb-back chairs, past the couch, through the kitchen, then back to the chairs. By the twentieth trip, her lovely house was beginning to feel like a prison, and Mari was still revving up in volume. By the fortieth trip, depression was trailing Laura like a ghost.

The doctor called it postpartum blues. He was full of jelly beans. She'd always been an upbeat sort of person, a life lover, never one to shy away from trouble. And she certainly didn't need a strange man cluttering up her kitchen to add to her problems. She would have no problems—just as soon as Mari quit crying.

"Could we approach this rationally?" she whispered to the screaming little one. "I'm trying the best I know how to be a perfect mother for you, darling. I would do anything for you, Mari, *anything*. Don't you know that? Dammit, was it the strawberries I ate this morning?"

Maybe Mari didn't like strawberry-flavored milk. Or eggs; Laura had eaten eggs for breakfast. Maybe the baby was too hot, too cold? Maybe she was bored, overstimulated, tired, not tired enough. Maybe the diaper was too tight, or not tight enough . . . oh, hell. Maybe she hated her mother?

"I take it the princess is having a royal tantrum today?"

Laura whirled to find Owen standing in the doorway, his hands planted on his hips and sunlight framing his jeans and striped shirt. She was so glad to see him that she could have cried, except that she already seemed to be sniffling. She blinked rapidly, thoroughly annoyed that his showing up mattered to her so much. "Pardon?"

"She does have a slight tendency to throw a temper tantrum whenever the wind blows the wrong way, doesn't she?" A wry smile played on his lips. "Hello, Laura. Ready to hit the road?"

He ambled familiarly toward the kitchen and returned seconds later with Mari's diaper bag slung over his shoulder. "Can't find your shoes."

Laura shook her head helplessly, motioning to Mari. "Where on earth could I take the baby when she's acting like *this?*"

"With me." He was astounded she'd even asked.

- 4 -

"I'M NOT SURE how I got talked into this drive," Laura remarked idly. Her eyes flickered from the contented baby in her arms to the rapidly passing scenery to Owen's face.

She hadn't noticed the laughter lines when she first met him. At the moment, his hair was lazily wind-ruffled and his hand light and relaxed on the steering wheel. The look was of a calm, easygoing man, and the look was totally misleading. Owen was dangerous. An extremely dangerous man who carted screaming babies around as a sideline—though, to give him credit, Mari had stopped crying the minute the engine purred beneath her. The baby liked expensive cars almost as much as Owen did.

Since he hadn't responded to her first comment, she tried a second. "I didn't expect to see you again. At least not in the middle of the day. Finding a little company to share coffee with at five o'clock in the morning . . . I understood that."

Owen's eyes had a rueful look as they glanced in the rearview mirror. No other woman would seriously believe that he'd been waking up at dawn only for her coffee.

"Laura?"

"Hmmm?"

"Cocoa futures dropped another three points last night. We're headed into the rainy season in Brazil, the time when flooding could ruin a cacao crop. Gary just informed me that we're facing a patent fight in the courts. And my twenty-year-old sister called last night to tell me all about her first love affair gone wrong. Now, on one of those days when the floods keep coming, you either have to start bailing or jump ship." He said gravely, "I opted to jump ship—at least for a few hours. And when I saw you coping with the princess in a tantrum, I figured I'd found a fellow sufferer looking for an escape."

Laura gave a little laugh. "Maybe you did."

"Is the baby wearing you to a frazzle?"

"Yes, darn it . . . but skip Mari. Is your little sister all right?"

Owen leaned back, his eyes glinting with amusement. "No one's okay after the first love affair ends, but, yes, Pat'll survive. The thing is, when you're twenty and getting hurt for the first time, you don't really *want* to survive." He added absently, "I wouldn't mind getting my hands on that boyfriend of hers for just five short minutes . . ."

Laura chuckled, but she shot him a thoughtful look. "Do your younger brothers and sisters put you through a lot of that kind of thing?"

"On occasion. When five of them were teenagers all at once . . . well, let's just say it's a miracle my parents stayed sane."

But then, they'd had help, Laura thought fleetingly. And wondered if Owen had ever had the chance to be just a little foolish and a little wild, like other teenagers. "When you talk about your brothers and sisters, you always sound so . . . protective."

"Do I?" Owen hesitated. "I guess I feel that way. My parents had to take care of the business as well as the kids. They needed help, and I was the oldest. My mother was ill for a time . . ." He leveled her a sideways glance. "I told you I'd diapered my share of babies."

But not that he'd had to, or that he'd been burdened with responsibility when he was so young. "And when did you learn to play?" she asked quietly.

"I'm learning right now." He grinned. "It's not all that hard, making up for lost time. And that's more than enough about me. When are you going to tell me about the princess?"

"Nothing to tell." Laura leaned back her head, her eyes sleepily regarding the flicker of sunlight through the passing trees. "I read all about it when

I was pregnant. The perfect-mother syndrome. Trying too hard instead of relaxing and using a little common sense. Of course, *I* was never going to fall into that pattern, because *I* was emotionally prepared." She turned her head, her expression deadpan. "I fell into it three and a half minutes after she was born."

"Laura, you're doing fine," Owen scolded gently.

"I would be, if she'd do just *one* thing by the book."

"Paige says the problem is that men write the baby books."

"Paige—that's Gary's wife? I keep getting the feeling I would like your sister-in-law."

"You will. In fact, you're going to meet her in five minutes."

Laura looked horrified. "Owen, I can't take the baby anywhere. She'll just cry . . ."

And Mari promptly started, the instant Owen switched off the engine. Unperturbed, he climbed out of the driver's seat and came around to the passenger side, his tall body blocking the view of a two-story colonial house with a yard full of tricycles and swing sets. His dark gray eyes leveled on Laura's. "Now, don't look stubborn."

"I am not going to inflict"—she raised her voice slightly, to be heard over Mari—"a screaming baby on a stranger."

"Paige won't mind."

"*I* do."

"Laura, my sister-in-law has three who can outshout the Grateful Dead. Now, relax—"

"Excuse me." A sprite of a woman with dark curly hair and huge brown eyes darted between them, laughter bubbling from her lips as she threw her arms around Owen and then promptly held them out for the baby. "You're Laura? And actually trying to out-argue my brother-in-law? God help you . . . Isn't she beautiful! How old, Laura?"

"I . . . four weeks."

"Sleeping all night yet?"

"Six hours last night."

Paige nodded. "Sounds about right. Another two weeks and you'll be out of the woods, but this is the hellish part, isn't it? You'd sell your soul for just one night of uninterrupted sleep. I read somewhere that the Chinese used it as torture during the war. Not letting prisoners of war sleep was such an easy way to drive them insane . . . Here, let me take her."

Ten minutes later, Laura was sitting at a counter in a bright yellow and white kitchen with a glass of iced tea in front of her. Paige hadn't stopped talking yet, and she still held the baby, who had stopped crying—probably because crying was pointless. The noise level was greater than anything Mari had ever been exposed to before, between trikes and baby walkers and toddlers whizzing by.

Standing in the doorway, Owen was listening to the chatter of the two-year-old perched on his shoulder, but he hadn't taken his eyes off Laura. Bringing her here was an attempt to steal some time alone with her. Paige wouldn't mind taking care of Mari for a few short hours while he spirited Laura away.

Only he'd forgotten—or failed to consider—how isolated Laura had been from feminine companionship since her recent move to the area. She was lapping up all the little reassurances from Paige that new mothers traditionally soak in from their mothers and sisters and friends.

"The doctor says she's only supposed to be fed every four hours."

"Bull. Show me one male doctor who's breast-fed a baby, and I'll show you a man worth listening to. I fed mine every two hours."

"Paige, she doesn't nap. I get so worried. All the books say she's supposed to."

"Have you tried—"

Owen didn't have the heart to interrupt, but his sister-in-law must have noticed his mournful expression, because she let out an abrupt peal of laughter and stood up. "All right! All right! We'll have other times to talk, won't we, Laura?"

Laura looked bewildered. Paige chuckled again, gave Mari a kiss on her rosy cheek, and said cheerfully, "You're stuck with me for a little bit, darlin'. Believe me, we'll get alone just fine."

Laura glanced at Owen suspiciously.

"We're leaving," he confirmed.

Clouds scudded across the sky in a hodgepodge of whimsical shapes. Leaves obscured most of them, and the sun sneaked through the greenery like a surprise, flickering on Laura's face, catching the soft lace at her throat, then dancing past her calico skirt to her bare legs crossed at the ankles. The blanket beneath her was soft; the earth beneath it just as warm and giving.

Somewhere in the park, teenagers were playing noisily with a Frisbee, but the sounds came from a long distance away. Here, a copse of white oaks offered a secluded haven of privacy, and delectable, unbuyable, precious quiet. Flat on her back, Laura closed her eyes in utter bliss.

"See?"

She peeked an eye open. There was a long, lanky frame next to her, stretched out with his arms behind his head, a blade of grass between his teeth, eyes closed. "Maybe," she said guardedly, "this was a good idea."

"It was a *great* idea."

"You need to learn how to do absolutely nothing for a change," she agreed.

Now, *that* wasn't fair, Owen thought with amusement. Laura needed to learn to relax as much as he did—and his impromptu kidnapping was working. Away from the baby, and with Mari given over to someone Laura trusted . . . yes, his lady lapped up peace and privacy.

Through shuttered lashes, his eyes roved over her supple form. A tumble of light hair spread in curls over the blanket, catching the gold of sunlight now and then. He'd stolen her shoes. Her feet were slim and tiny. He couldn't see nearly enough of her bare legs under the calico skirt, but he could make out the shape of her thighs and that tiny mound of a stomach that so embarrassed her. She wore a white blouse with a little froth of white lace at the throat and cuffs, fastened with small pearl buttons, her breasts straining the fabric despite the demure design.

She could have been from another age. The age of pirates and virgins, of rakes and innocents. He propped himself up on an elbow, carefully respecting the six-inch distance she'd so deliberately established between them. He wanted to ravish her, steal her away, strip off the concealing layers of clothing inch by inch.

"No."

She spoke the word like a proclamation, but her eyes were still closed. He raised one dark eyebrow. "No, what?"

The smallest warm breeze touched her face. The earth smelled rich; the forest smells were hypnotic, life smells, soft smells. She could hear the rustle of leaves brushing together, see the shimmer of sunlight behind her closed eyelids, taste summer in the air. The man next to her was more potent than all of that; Laura could perceive him with all five senses. "You didn't kidnap me," she said lightly, her eyes still closed.

"No?"

"You didn't bring me here to relax either, Reesling."

His lips twisted in a crooked smile. "You think not?" He leaned closer, his fingers lightly combing through her hair.

"I know not. You're looking for someone to play with, Owen." Her lashes fluttered open, her eyes that special blue-green, endless, fathomless. She saw in his eyes exactly what she'd expected to see. Wanting, bold and bright. "And I came with you willingly," she said casually, "to remind you of a few things."

"Such as?" Like silk, the strands curled around his fingers. He edged a leg closer, bridging that six-inch invisible wall without yet touching her.

"Such as, new babies make for impossible love affairs."

"Difficult, yes."

"And ladies who've just had babies have healing stitches. In awkward places."

He smothered a laugh.

Laura kept the deliberately light tone, but her eyes were serious, suddenly filled with anxiety. "Owen, there are lots of women out there. Women with time, women with nice flat stomachs, women who are prettier, smarter..." She took a breath, and suddenly couldn't try to make it funny anymore. "I deeply appreciate what you've done for me. You've just... been there, through a rough week, and I—"

"You foolish woman." He leaned over her, blocking the sun, his face all angles and shadows and angry gray eyes. "You're the one who's been there for me this week, not the other way around. You were stuck listening to my whole list of woes—"

"I wasn't *stuck*."

"Being you, no." His eyes softened. "You show caring naturally, sweet; I don't think you could help it if you tried—but if you really believe the only thing going on between us is a mutual-support society, we'd better clear that up right now."

The sun and woods disappeared altogether when
Owen's head dipped down. His mouth was warm
and sweet, like wild honey. The fierce, wooing pressure of his kiss contrasted to the lightest stroke of
his fingertips on her bare throat. She wasn't prepared for the sweep of exquisite emotions that en-
gulfed her. It had seemed such a brilliant idea, to
come with him and tell him the truth. Cards-on-the-
table honesty . . . but Owen seemed to know a different kind of honesty.

His fingertips caressed the vulnerable hollow in
her throat with the whispery touch of a lover. His
tongue thrust into the dark secret corners of her
mouth, plundering with the intimacy of a lover. She
lay still, absolutely still. Fire warmed her skin, but
ice cooled her veins; or perhaps it was the other
way around. It didn't matter. She'd been afraid of
what would happen if he touched her, and even if
she died from the fire of passion and the ice of fear
she would not give in.

A throaty chuckle escaped his throat, a wicked
sound on a quiet afternoon. Her eyes flew open.
"That'll never work with me, you know," he whispered, "but it's rather fun that you even want to try.
I've kissed you before, have you forgotten? Fight
it if you want to. Fight it just as long and as hard
as you want to, Laura . . ."

She would have delivered a long, sound lecture
on arrogance, but he was kissing her again. Different kisses. Teasing kisses, his lips just brushing
hers. His tongue defined the shape of her bottom

lip with feathered softness. His fingers brushed back her hair, over and over, slow, lazy movements, a tender touch.

The pulse jumped in her throat when his palm gradually stroked from her throat to the swell of her breast, down to her ribs, down . . . Her hand jerked up, clamped on his wrist.

"Don't," she whispered haltingly.

There was no give in his voice. "You have every stitch of your clothes on. We're in a public park. You're not afraid of anything I'm going to do here."

"Owen—"

"We're not going far, love. Just a short excursion down a very private road for a minute or two. Just to make sure you know . . . it doesn't happen this way between any other two people. This is happening only for us, Laura. Don't be afraid to show me what you feel, what I want you to feel . . ."

He didn't understand. He couldn't possibly understand. There were risks she couldn't take again. She tried to tell him, opening her lips, but his mouth was waiting for her, pressing on hers, coaxing her head back against the blanket. His leg insinuated itself between hers, and she felt herself sinking. The weight of him, the pressure of his arousal, his warmth, the fierce, endless kisses . . .

Fear dissolved into intensely powerful emotions, a terrible surge of need to be held, to be wanted, to be taken by this man, now, here, before the fear came back again. Her senses were making insatiable demands, to touch and be touched, and she seemed to be trembling, inside, outside, all over.

Her fingers skidded over his arms, his shoulders, groping and awkward, trying to hold on. His touch was fire, and she was burning. She heard his whispered *"yes,"* as if she'd done something right when everything she was doing was wrong. She knew it was; Peter had told her over and over how inadequate she was as a lover. But Peter suddenly seemed someone from a far-distant past; Owen was... Owen. Here, now, immediate. And as if he were the only man she'd ever known, her mouth searched for his, found it, savored as he'd savored, crushed as he'd crushed.

Owen's palm slid under her skirt and glided intimately over her thigh. Under a tangle of fabric, she felt him cup her bottom and hold her hard against him. The breath whooshed from her lungs in a hoarse, murmured plea, and she heard an answering groan escape Owen.

In time, he pushed down her skirt; his kisses turned gentle. His hands soothed instead of stroked, although the beat in his Adam's apple was unsteady when he looked down at her. "Do you have any idea how beautiful you are?" he whispered.

A faint flush darkened her cheeks. He smiled. His arms went around her, holding her, like a velvet cage, his chin nuzzling the top of her head. "I thought I could behave myself if I brought you to a public place. Obviously, I was wrong." He tilted back his head. "You're not safe, you know."

"Owen—"

"Yes, I know all about your stitches," he said dryly. "Just ... stay still for a minute. Let me hold you."

He held her until he again felt her relax in his arms. His eyes turned pensive, thoughtful. She so fiercely held back that inner Laura. But when she let loose, he had treasure. She was richly abandoned in giving—loving and needing love like no other woman he'd known.

"Owen?"

"Hmmm?"

"Your arm has to be cramped."

"It is. And your baby is undoubtedly getting hungry." He sighed. Moments later, they gathered up the blanket and slipped on their shoes. On the drive home, he couldn't stop stealing glances at her. Her hair was wind-tumbled; there was a sleepy flush on her cheeks that he knew he'd put there. Still, her eyes shied away from his; she was careful not to touch him.

At a traffic light, he leaned over to press a whimsical kiss on her nose. "Stop thinking, would you?" he teased, but there was a layer of seriousness in his voice.

"I'm afraid . . . I misled you," she said quietly. "Owen . . ."

"Know something?"

"What?"

"I'd like to believe we're past pretending. I'd like to believe you and I don't need any kind of pretense between us."

He reached out a hand, and after a moment's hesitation she took it, perhaps because she badly wanted to believe, as he did, that they had something special together.

Still, shadows clung to her mind; she felt a rush

of nameless anxiety. Already, he meant too much to her. It was easier to believe she cared for him because it was a time in her life when she needed someone—anyone—just to be there. But no other man was like Owen. He sparked feelings she shouldn't feel; he made being wanted seem like a gift.

Laura fed Mari in Paige's back bedroom, and when she returned to the kitchen, there was a picnic-style dinner spread out on the table. Toddlers were helping themselves to vegetables and dip; Owen was standing with a beer in one hand and a hefty plate of potato salad and ham in the other. Paige promptly stole Mari from Laura's arms, flitted around the kitchen putting more food on the table, and never stopped talking.

"*Eat* now. There's no point in waiting for Gary. My Dad's got him adding a room to their house—they take advantage, I swear. The baby was an angel, did I tell you that? And, Laura, you can see I'm set up for babies—I'm also tied down here as sure as if there were a rope around my neck; have you ever tried to take three toddlers to the grocery store? So I thought up this great plan while you and Owen were gone. From now on, you come over here on Tuesday mornings; you watch my monsters for an hour so I can shop; then *you* can take off while I watch Mari. Life is so much easier when you know other mothers."

Laura listened and occasionally got in a word of her own; her glance kept wandering to Owen and she smiled. From across the room, he hadn't taken his eyes off her. She felt his look, like the pull of a magnet, like a secret that no one else knew or could even sense. His mouth was twisted in a patient grin as he listened to his sister-in-law's bubbling chatter, but his eyes communicated private messages to Laura.

Mine, Laura.

The next time, there isn't going to be anyone around.

Button by button, I want to take that blouse off . . .

A two-year-old climbed on Laura's lap; she hugged her, still listening to Paige, still conscious of Owen as if they were alone.

". . . It isn't colic, you know. Colic is when a baby's stomach knots up harder than a rock; you can tell. Mari wasn't like that, and some babies just cry more than others. I promise it will pass; all the terrible things pass—that's a guarantee. In fact, the *only* guarantee with children is that they trade in one terrible stage for another."

Still talking, Paige trailed the two of them to the car. Reluctantly, she released Mari to Laura's arms and waved until the car was out of sight.

Mari slept while they drove; Laura leaned her head back. "Your sister-in-law—I love her," she mentioned.

"I hoped you would." He loved the look of Laura. She'd had some rest, a break from the baby, a dinner she didn't have to prepare. It took so little to bring out her natural smile. A glow of contentment touched her features in the waning light of early evening, a sensual loveliness, a freshness of spirit. He said casually, "I want you, Laura."

"Yes." Unsurprised by his abrupt comment, she leaned her head back, her lips curling in an elusive smile. "Owen, you're nuts."

"I don't think so."

"Do I have to remind you again that I just had a baby?"

"So we wait. I never had in mind pushing you that fast."

One eyebrow arched delicately. "Of course you did. You're used to moving in fast, Owen. Making decisions, then acting on them."

He paused. "I think," he said quietly, "you are, too."

"Not about . . . people."

"Yes, about people. And your work, and your life. I think you're like me, Laura—when you know something's right, you don't normally hesitate to face your feelings honestly."

Laura sighed. "Yes," she said softly, "but this is different, Owen. You're different. I don't feel around you the way I expected to feel—" Around any man, she almost said, but a lump formed in her throat. Weeks ago, she would never have believed how fiercely she could want a stranger. Or how deliciously frightening it felt to be wanted in return.

"Laura." Owen's voice had the nectar of caring. "Tell me what you're afraid of, sweet. Give me a chance to share it. Or am I completely wrong in believing that you feel as strongly as I do when we're together?"

She turned her head, her cheek against the soft

upholstery, studying his strong profile. "No," she said simply. "I feel ... good with you. You must know that. But there are things you don't know, Owen, things I can't change, things that have happened to me. I can't promise you that I'm ready for a relationship..."

"I'm not asking for a promise. I'm only asking that you give us time."

She closed her eyes and desperately willed away a dozen haunting anxieties. "You're not going to be patient," she accused him wryly.

He said nothing. He didn't need to. Her comment had been a tentative yes, and they both knew it. At a traffic light, his hands reached out, gently stroked Mari's sleeping head for a moment, then slid down to rest possessively on Laura's thigh.

The light was fading by the time he pulled up her drive. He half frowned, noting the small blue car parked beside the house before she did. Laura's head was bent over Mari, as she pulled a small knit cap over the baby's head.

He reached for the diaper bag, saying nothing for a minute as he noticed the tall form of a man standing near the door of Laura's house. He was blond, well over six feet, a rangy, big-limbed man in sweat shirt and jeans. He was also good-looking, which made Owen's eyes narrow reflectively.

"Maybe by some miracle I can get out of this car without waking up the baby," Laura whispered, chuckling until she glanced at him. "What's wrong?"

"Nothing," he said reassuringly. "You have company."

"What? How could I? I don't know anyone around

here!" Her head whipped toward her house.

Owen couldn't believe how fast her expression changed. The look of soft laughter disappeared and was replaced by a mask of utter stillness. The color drained from her face, and her arms tightened around the baby.

Without question, Owen knew the man had to be her former husband.

- 5 -

"LAURA?"

Her eyes jumped to his, suddenly remote and opaque, telling him nothing of what she was feeling. "It's my ex-husband," she said shortly. "Unexpected—but then that's always expected where Peter is concerned." She ducked her head, gathering the rest of the baby gear. "Owen—"

"You want me to leave?"

"It isn't that. I doubt he'll stay very long, but I don't want to put you in a position where you'll feel . . . awkward."

"To hell with that," he muttered impatiently. Exactly like her, to worry about his feelings. And Laura was suddenly wearing pride like a mask.

Carefully, so as not to wake the baby, she reached for the door handle. "I heard that."

"Did you?"

She forced a smile. "Lord, you're protective," she said gently. "This is nothing to worry about, Owen. I can handle Peter. But meeting him would be uncomfortable for you, and I don't want you to feel obligated to stay."

He didn't want her fake smiles, and he didn't want the invisible wall she'd just put between them. "Look, do you *mind* if I meet your ex?"

"No, of course not." She reached again for the door. "You'll undoubtedly like each other." She took a breath. "Everyone likes Peter."

Owen was more inclined to break the man's head than to like him, and in that general mood climbed out of the car.

"Laura?"

The guy had a sexy, melodious voice. Another good reason to want to deck him.

"Peter, I didn't expect you . . ."

"I'm sorry. But I was afraid if I called ahead, you wouldn't let me come. You wouldn't see me when you were in the hospital."

Twin spots of color stained Laura's cheeks as she introduced the two men.

Owen extended his hand, which was immediately seized by a damp grip that startled him. Close up, Owen could see the faint sheen of nervous perspiration on her ex-husband's forehead, and mentally frowned.

"I apologize if I interrupted something," Peter

said quietly. "As Laura can tell you, I travel all over the country. When I happened to be close enough to see the baby, I just took the chance..."

"You want to hold her?" Laura asked crisply.

Peter's eyes clamped on Laura's. Gingerly, he took Mari, holding her as if she were a carton of eggs. "She looks... beautiful," he whispered.

Owen could barely keep his eyes off the man. The sun had dropped behind the treetops, but even in the fading light he had a clear picture. Peter was big, not heavy so much as brawny. Square, clean-cut features were framed by a thick crop of blond hair. This was not a man who treated life lightly; deep lines of strain and concentration furrowed his forehead. He bent his head to his daughter for a moment, and Owen saw the fierce look of love he expected to feel for a child of his own one day.

The urge to murder him abated somewhat. Her ex-husband—Owen had had visions of a wife beater, a violent man, a cruel man. Something to justify Laura's severing of the marriage in the middle of her pregnancy, something to explain why she shied away from a certain kind of touch. Though Peter was big and muscular he was not an abusive man; Owen would have staked his life on that. And he looked at Laura as if she were special. When he glanced at Owen, his mouth widened in a definitely boyish grin. "She *is* the most beautiful baby you've ever seen, isn't she?"

"A princess," Owen agreed. No disagreement about *that*.

"She's been good?" Peter turned to Laura again.

"You've been all right? I was worried about you after the birth. I wanted you to have help, Laura, but every check I sent you—"

"I've been fine, and she's been an angel. I didn't need any help, honestly. Everything's going well. Wonderful, in fact." Laura's smile was as brilliant and fake as paste diamonds. She moved toward the door, away from both men. "Come in. I'll make a quick pot of coffee."

Alone in the kitchen, Laura couldn't find the coffee. It was on the shelf where she always kept it. Spoons clattered together; she had no cream— and then remembered that neither Owen nor Peter took cream. She spilled the sugar as she poured it into a porcelain cup, then couldn't find a tray . . . In the other room, Mari let out a protesting wail. Laura bolted for the door, and then stopped. Peter had the right to hold his daughter. And Owen—as long as Owen was there, she knew she didn't have to worry about anything happening to the baby.

Bracing her hands on the counter, her head bowed, Laura claimed just a minute alone. Peter's low baritone filtered back to her; she heard him chuckle at something Owen said. The men were getting along fine.

It mattered. She didn't want Owen to think she'd married a bastard. Peter wasn't a bastard, and Laura had her share of pride . . . a pride she was holding on to by a thread, at the moment. *Oh, no, you don't. You're going to handle this, and you're going to handle it well.*

Obviously, she'd known she'd have to see Peter

again because of Mari. It was just . . . if she'd known he was coming, she could have prepared herself emotionally. As it was, a volcano of memories threatened to erupt inside her. She'd forgotten . . . too much. Her relationship with Peter had been an exercise in humiliation. She'd felt as if she were imposing on a man who only pretended to want and need her.

She hadn't been very smart. She'd been even less smart in the woods that afternoon with Owen. Grown women didn't still believe in Santa Claus. Pretending she could start a serious relationship . . . no. One look at Peter had shot to bits any illusions she might have had about embarking on a new sexual relationship. Wanting was easy, but to need someone wasn't enough—not unless you were needed back. In time, yes. In time, she wanted to believe she would have the courage to seek love again, but not when the baby needed all her emotional energy, not until she had built up enough strength to spring back from the blow Peter had dealt her.

Pull yourself together, Laura.

Abruptly, she stiffened her spine, schooled her features, and opened the refrigerator. When Owen suddenly appeared in the doorway, she was wearing a cheerful, calm expression . . . but she could feel a betraying color jump to her cheeks when he noticed the bottle of wine in her hand. "The coffee's almost ready, but I thought at this time of night I should probably offer wine as well."

"Yes." They both knew that she was the one who needed the wine—and that she hadn't touched the bottle since the afternoon of the accident. "I'll pour you a glass and carry the tray."

"You don't have to do that."

So they were back to you-don't-have-to-do-that's. Owen considered taking the bottle from her hand and smashing it. He considered snatching Laura up and spiriting her off. And he again considered smashing Peter's face in, for whatever hell he'd put her through to make her as tense and miserable as a kitten suspended over a well.

Instead, he poured a glass of wine for her, followed her in with the tray, and deliberately took the chair between Laura and Peter. When he had her alone, she was going to talk, whether she wanted to or not.

Until then, he lazily stretched out his legs and leaned back in the chair, communicating in body language that this was a hunky-dory evening, that no one had any reason to be upset, and that anyone who tried to cross the barrier of his legs to get to Laura was not going to live long.

As Owen initiated a smooth flow of conversation with her ex-husband, Laura gradually settled back on the couch.

It clearly mattered to Laura that he like Peter, and after talking with him for better than a half-hour, Owen's first impression confirmed that Peter was a quiet, genial man with a gentle sense of humor. He hid his nervousness well, neither forced conversation nor avoided it, and met Owen's eyes head on. All traits Owen normally liked in others.

Not in Peter. Owen never trusted a man he

couldn't fathom. Peter showed no trace of jealousy
or surprise at finding a strange man with Laura. In
his shoes, Owen would have been off the wall. And
every time Laura opened her mouth, Peter looked
up with a genuinely warm smile.

Owen was not happy.

"You've done a beautiful job here," Peter said
softly to Laura, his eyes flickering around the room.
"There's the lighthouse clock." He grinned. "I remember that Sunday afternoon when you were trying
to get the tarnish off that thing. The whole apartment
reeked of polish."

Laura twirled the stem of the wineglass. "Your
work is going well?"

"Sure. Travis and Judy are always asking about
you."

"I miss them," she admitted. "And Mike, he's
doing okay?"

"You know Mike. He's forever thinking up some
great wild scheme, but it's always talk. Steve's wife
is pregnant."

"Is she?" Laura took a sip, then put the wineglass
down. Old friends from the music world . . . she
missed them all. She knew Peter was bringing them
up to remind her of people she'd—from his view-
point—casually tossed out of her life. Peter had the
gift of gently, gently poking at sores that were almost healed, until suddenly they were raw wounds
again.

And Owen was vibrating with all the tension of
a caged tiger. She could barely look at him. She
wanted to believe she was handling the conversation

rather well; she wanted to believe she looked composed and calm, but every time she felt Owen's eyes rest on her, she knew she wasn't succeeding. Owen was too damned perceptive.

"And my parents said they tried to contact you several times, Laura. I can't imagine that you couldn't find the time to at least drop them a letter..."

"Yes." Another raw wound. Peter's parents had been dear to her, as had so many of their friends. She must have looked callous to all of them when she severed contact without a word. And she must look the same way to Owen.

For some foolish reason, she'd set down the wineglass, leaving her nothing to do with her hands. She quickly picked it up again. "I should have discussed Mari with you before, Peter. Of course, you have the right to see the baby, but it's awkward while I'm nursing her. You can only take her for an hour or two at a time, and you're not even living near here..."

That fast, the atmosphere changed. Peter never came out fighting, of course; he just put more velvet in his voice. "Naturally, it would have been easier for me to see her if you hadn't moved."

She took a breath, feeling sick inside as she hadn't felt sick in a long time. Sick and sad and somehow defensive. She hadn't deserted friends or ignored his parents or even moved by choice. If she'd stayed, people would have asked questions, questions she couldn't answer. Not because of her own pride but because of Peter's ... and because of the baby in his arms, with her father's intense blue eyes. "I realize that my moving made it more difficult for you."

"Which was very clever of you, if you didn't want me to have much contact with her."

She was beginning to feel hounded, yet Peter was wearing a hurt look in his eyes, and glancing at Owen as if to ask for his sympathy. "Peter, you must know I didn't move to keep you from seeing her."

"No? Well, I'll manage somehow, regardless," he said quietly. "I still don't understand about the hospital. You called me when the baby was born, but wouldn't let me see you. All I wanted to do was congratulate you, Laura. Was that so hard to understand?"

She touched her fingers to her temples. His velvet tone, his soulful eyes—somehow, Peter always made her feel as if she had done something wrong. "No, of course not." Distressed, Laura's voice came out low, almost trembly. "I apologize, but at the time—"

Carefully, he shifted the baby and stood up. "She's my daughter, too, Laura."

"I've never denied that!"

"But you'd like to."

"You probably have a long drive back, to wherever the hell you're going," Owen interrupted cheerfully.

There was a moment of silence, not long. Owen stared at Peter; Peter stared at Owen and then rather abruptly handed the baby to Laura. As if sensing the tension in the atmosphere, Mari opened her eyes and let out an irritated yell.

"What's wrong with her?" Peter asked immediately.

"Nothing," Laura said swiftly. "She's getting hungry, and she needs to be changed." She darted an accusatory glance at Owen for jumping in. Lovingly cradling the baby to her shoulder, she said to Peter, "After that, she'll sleep through the night. There's no point in your staying." The baby's plaintive cries drowned out his answer, and when Peter moved to the front door, Laura turned toward the stairs to the left.

When she was out of sight, the two men stood facing each other. The flare of anger in Peter's eyes expressed the first honest emotion Owen had seen so far, and gave him a reason to respect the man.

"I'm staying until I've had a word with her in private," Peter said flatly.

Owen shook his head. "Nope. You're not." His tone was still pleasant. "You had your word with her. And succeeded in making Laura feel bad—which is undoubtedly what you wanted to do."

"That's ridiculous. You don't know anything about Laura and me."

"You're absolutely right. I know nothing about you, about why Laura moved, about why she wouldn't see you in the hospital, about why she felt she had to drop old friends who were evidently important to her—but I do know about people who lay subtle guilt trips on others. You brought up every subject you knew would hurt her, didn't you? Have a nice drive."

"I think you've misunderstood," Peter said stiffly.

"Sure I have."

A muscle in Peter's jaw tightened, but just that abruptly, he backed off. Five seconds later, he left the house, slamming the screen door. Owen stood there, rubbing the back of his neck wearily, and then squinted up the steps to the loft.

He expected Laura was furious with him.

She certainly had reason to be. He'd interfered with all the subtlety of a bulldozer, and he wasn't proud of himself. He'd had every intention of being civil to her ex-husband. It just hadn't worked out that way.

Laura was his. He hadn't realized quite how much he cared until Peter tried to needle her. In other circumstances, maybe the guy was as gut-likable as he'd originally seemed—but a man didn't lay a pile of emotional baggage on a vulnerable woman. Laura was far from her physical and emotional strongest, this soon after the birth. No one was going to hurt her. If that was a rather cavemanish attitude, Owen was guilty.

He decided to give her a few minutes to cool down. Wandering toward the kitchen, he opened cupboards one after another. He wanted scotch, but it was one of those rare times he'd even settle for bourbon. As he anticipated, he found nothing.

When the baby finished nursing, Laura rocked her until Mari nodded off to sleep. She hadn't turned on a lamp. Pale moonlight flooded in the half-open window, spilling over the soft yellow carpeting, the gay pattern of yellow and white unicorns on the wall. Mari had both a regular crib and an infant cradle with a soft yellow canopy. It was a wonderful room, fit for a princess.

Unfortunately, the princess was sound asleep, and didn't need any more rocking. Laura would have liked an excuse to stay right where she was. Ten minutes before, she'd heard Owen's footsteps on the loft stairs. He hadn't looked in, but she knew he was waiting somewhere.

She laid the baby in the cradle and waited a minute. If Mari wanted to be a sweetheart, she could wake up again ... but Laura knew she wouldn't. When Mari cried, she screamed; when she slept, an earthquake wouldn't rouse her.

She had the fleeting thought that earthquakes would be easier to deal with than Owen. She was darn furious with him for virtually ordering Peter out of the house, but that wasn't the only reason she dreaded having to face him. The hardest task would be reneging on the commitment she'd made to him that afternoon.

Nervously smoothing her hair, she left the baby's door ajar, took a step into the hall, and halted abruptly. The ceiling light was on in her bedroom, casting a rectangular pool of yellow light into the narrow hall.

When she took a tentative step inside, her lips parted in surprise. Her mattress and box springs were standing upright against the wall. Owen was lying flat on his back with the frame of her William and Mary four-poster laid out in a square, a screwdriver in his hand.

"Close Mari's door, will you? I can't guarantee this'll be quiet."

"Owen—" She hadn't expected to find him in her bedroom, much less . . . working.

"Why didn't you tell me you'd been sleeping on the floor all this time? Close Mari's door. Then if you'll hold up the sides while I screw . . ." He lifted his head from the floor, his dark eyes daring her to argue with him.

She debated several seconds before going back to close Mari's door. Returning, she grasped the bed frame while Owen screwed the parts together. About a dozen lame conversational possibilities came to mind, but none seemed to get past her dry throat. Owen had no such problem. He delivered his comments military fashion, so fast she had no time to dissemble.

"That too heavy for you?"

"No."

"That man still cares about you."

"Yes." She wasn't looking at him.

"He never physically harmed you."

Her eyes flickered up in surprise. "Peter would never physically harm anyone."

"Let that down, would you? And hand me another screw—I have *never* seen screws like this one."

"They're old—it's the way they used to put beds together . . ."

"The baby's room is fit for a princess. When were you going to get around to your own? Dammit, you're entitled to a little comfort—and you sure as hell have the sense to know you need your rest."

He was angry, it seemed. Beads of sweat danced across his forehead as he struggled with the heavy frame. Halfway through the project, he paused long enough to strip off his shirt and toss it aside.

Laura took an extra-deep breath. Bare-chested, Owen was rather intimidating. Peter was heavier; Owen was all sinew, his chest hair thicker, springier. Like everything else he did, he took on the bed project at full steam, all concentration and determination. His body moved with sleek grace, quiet and sure. Laura felt her eyes straying again and again to his chest, his throat, the smooth ripple of muscle in his upper arms and shoulders. Owen was a virile man. She couldn't help being sexually aware of him; and felt momentarily grateful that he was angry. Anger she could deal with.

Only he didn't appear angry when the frame was finally finished and he sprang to his feet. In fact, his tone was decidedly gentle when he said, "Now, *don't* try to help me lift these."

He heaved the box springs onto the frame, then hauled the mattress into place. Immediately, Laura hurried forward to straighten the tumble of sheets and blankets. Unmade beds and Owen—no.

As if he knew what she was thinking, his mouth was twisted in a wry smile when she turned to face him. He waited a moment, standing in that doorway, his eyes piercing and sharp on her wary features. "You didn't do much with that glass of wine downstairs except twirl it around. Do you want me to go down and bring it back up here?" *Before we talk* was understood.

"No. I don't need wine." She changed her mind abruptly. She needed . . . a lot of wine. Owen was busy suddenly. He shrugged on his shirt, not bothering with the buttons, then flicked off the harsh ceiling light and switched on the softer lamp at her bedside. "Owen . . ." She drew a breath. "I'm afraid I made a mistake this afternoon. In . . . letting you believe that I—"

"I like this room, with the slanted ceiling and the four-poster. It's like you, Laura—or it will be when you get curtains up. Blue and white again? You like blue and white."

She said helplessly, "Yes."

He slipped off his shoes and, as casually as if this were his own house, fluffed the pillows and flopped on the comforter. "Over here." He motioned to the pillow next to him.

She sighed with exasperation. "I think not."

"Beds are good places to talk," he coaxed.

"Said the spider to the fly. Owen—"

"Now, I can understand your feelings," Owen said mildly, throwing an arm behind his head. "You think I want you over here just so I can get my hands on you—and I would love to have my hands on you, sweet, but not now. Nothing's going to happen on this bed but a little easy conversation . . . with you providing most of it. But if worse comes to worst and I can't control my baser impulses, you can always remind me of your stitches again."

"That's supposed to be comforting?" But she could feel the corners of her mouth starting to turn up. What she had to say to him wasn't going to be easy, but she couldn't keep on feeling traumatized and nervous when Owen was so ceaselessly *natural*. "Owen, thank you for putting up the bed."

"You're welcome. I've earned a back rub. Collectible at another time." He raised a pillow in the air as if presenting a trophy, then deliberately squashed it down in the center of the bed. "See? A bundling board. The thing the Puritans used to keep the sexes separate in bed. Isn't that what they were called?"

She sighed, giving in, moving quietly to the other side of the bed only because she couldn't continue to just stand there. There was no place else to sit. "Somehow, I have trouble believing you want to talk about early New England courting customs," she said dryly.

"It'll do." Until she relaxed. So gingerly she sat down next to him. So gingerly she leaned back against a pillow a good twelve inches from any part of his body. And very quietly, Owen reached up to switch off the lamp next to the bed. Darkness flooded the room. "So . . . bundling boards were a courting custom?"

"Actually . . . no. Bundling boards were just a way of dealing with bed shortages. In those days, there were too many people and not enough beds, so unmarried men and women had to sleep together, separated by a bundling board." Laura hesitated, then determinedly went on. "Courting customs were more interesting, actually. When a boy came calling, they used to tie him up in bed with the girl."

"The *Puritans?*"

"Funny, isn't it. The father would hog-tie them and then wrap them up in separate blankets. They weren't supposed to touch, just talk. It was really the only way to give a young couple privacy—New England nights were cold; the rest of the family huddled around a fire that didn't provide enough warmth as it was." Laura took a breath. "Why did you turn out the light?"

"So you'd find it easier to talk. Why'd you divorce him?"

"I'll bet little boys learned to untie knots before they were weaned in those times."

Owen turned his head on the pillow. "All right, Laura. We'll start with an easier question. How did you meet him?"

She was glad he'd turned out the light. Moonlight poured into the room, and the scent of flowers and grass and earth drifted through the open window. She was unbelievably tired, and the privacy of darkness was soothing. The man next to her, in a strange way, was also soothing. She could see the shape of Owen's long legs, the stretch of dark chest, the shadow of his night beard by moonlight. His eyes stayed on her, steady and relentlessly . . . gentle.

The temptation was incredibly strong to reach out, to be enfolded in his long, strong arms, to believe in love again the way he'd almost made her believe that afternoon.

"Laura? Are you still carrying a torch for him?"

She found her voice suddenly. There was no hesitation. "No torch."

"There could be. The divorce hasn't been final for that long."

"I don't care if it was over yesterday. There's no torch."

"Good." Owen let out a massive sigh, revealing he hadn't been so sure of that as he'd let on. "So why is it so hard for you to talk about him, honey?"

That answer, too, was very simple. "It's an ugly story, Owen. And I don't want to tell you . . . ugly things."

Like a thief, he stole the pillow between them and sent it hurtling to the far side of the room. She'd *known* he couldn't be trusted, and mute betrayal was in her eyes when he leaned over her. "Arms up," he said swiftly.

He did it for her, roped her arms around his neck. Faster than she could breathe, he had cradled her close, one long leg pinning hers, his fingers brushing her hair into the pillow. "Now," he murmured, "fast and sweet, love. Let's just get it over with. And let's hear no more foolishness about 'ugly things.' Know right now that nothing you say or do could be ugly to me, Laura, so get that thought right out of your head."

"You don't know."

"I know. Dammit, give me an enemy to fight, Laura. You think I couldn't see you pull away from me the minute he appeared?"

Crystals blurred her eyes. "He isn't an enemy. He's a kind, warm man, Owen. A good man, and from the day I met him, I never doubted that he loved me." Owen gently brushed a tear from her cheek with the pad of his thumb. Suddenly, the words came out in a rush. "I was a virgin when I met him. A stupid thing to be at twenty-two years of age, but my family had always traveled so much ... and maybe I was afraid of strong feelings I hadn't learned to handle yet. Maybe I just needed to believe I was loved first."

"Go on," he said softly.

But she couldn't. There was a lump locked in her throat that simply wouldn't go away. "You just met him," she said finally. "You saw him. He's a big man, a gentle man. He's artistic by nature, but he's also muscular. He watches football; he plays racquetball; he drinks beer—Owen, I'm not so sure I can tell you the rest."

Suddenly, Owen wasn't either. Laura was trembling; in the moonlight he could see the waxen paleness of her features.

"It seemed fine at first," she said with artificial brightness. "I didn't have a lot of experience, so it was hard for me to judge ... certain things. I thought we had a good marriage. He was good to me; he encouraged me to do things I wanted to do with my life; he was considerate in a thousand ways. It was just ... We were married more than three years. And sometimes weeks would go by, and then sometimes months ..."

Owen gently shifted up on one elbow. Leaning over her, he quietly combed back her hair over and over, his eyes never leaving her face. He was listening to raw pain.

"I found him in bed with another man," she said with abrupt harshness. "Isn't that a stitch, Owen? I thought that only happened to people ... on the fringe. Gay bars and men who dressed funny. It's not supposed to happen to just ordinary people."

"My God, honey—" He moved to draw her close, but Laura pushed his arms away.

"He never told me before we were married, or later, and heaven knows, I never once guessed." She shook her head with a hoarse laugh. "That kind of naiveté is a joke in this day and age. He expected me to understand. I didn't understand. I *don't* understand—"

"Laura. Enough, love. You don't have to tell me anymore . . ."

Tears streamed down her cheeks. "He didn't want the divorce. He'd produced Mari, hadn't he? That was *normal,* wasn't it? But it only took five minutes of . . . seeing him like that to explain so much. Why we'd lived like brother and sister most of the time. How inadequate I'd been as a woman for him. Living a 'normal' life was terribly important to him; he said he loved me and he'd tried—and if it hadn't worked, it was my fault. He kept saying I was 'not woman enough.' Do you want to get involved with a woman who's 'not woman enough,' Owen? Please. Just get out of here and leave me alone."

She sprang from the bed before he could stop her. Arms locked around her chest, she retreated to a dark corner in the bedroom. Owen could hear her breathing, haunted and uneven. "Please . . . just go," she whispered.

Owen's response was swift and immediate. "No way."

- 6 -

OWEN SWUNG HIS legs off the bed, his eyes trying
to pierce the shadows where Laura was standing.
He caught a glint of her moonlit hair, the curve of
her shouders, the utter stillness of her. Every pulse,
every muscle, every nerve in his body wanted to
go to her, hold her . . . dammit, make love to her.

For the tick of a second there was silence. Unfortunately, his lady wasn't physically ready to be
made love to. And Owen had the fleeting intuition
that emotionally, too, she would reject his touch
right now. Any man's touch.

His head reeled with the implications of the story
she'd told him. He had a clear picture of what the
marriage had been like for her. Too clear. And

whether or not Laura wanted to be held, he had a very good idea that she needed to be.

"Owen . . . please go home."

"Yes." He crossed the dark room in four long strides, took her hands, and pulled her back with him toward the bed. She stiffened at his touch, but she didn't fight him.

"You don't need to stay just because you think . . . I'm upset. I'm not upset—"

"I know you're not." Sitting down, he drew her on his lap and simply let his warmth penetrate the trembling chill of her. She was upset and exhausted and very easily overpowered with gentleness. Her cheek sank on his shoulder, and his heart ached, loving her.

"It was all over a long time ago. I feel so foolish . . . telling you any of it. It's my problem, not yours. I want you to go home, Owen."

"Yes." Her hair was tangled, falling over her forehead. He brushed it back, his lips on the crown of her head.

Laura made a move to get off his lap, but his arms simply tightened around her. She sighed, feeling impossibly confused. She should be leading him downstairs, not wrapping her arms around him as if he were the only safe harbor in a hurricane. She wanted to talk to him calmly and sensibly, and instead heard her voice come out as shaky as a butterfly in the wind. "All I meant to talk about was the two of us, and that has nothing to do with Peter. I never meant to tell you any of that . . ."

"Yes."

"It's just that for a while . . . I have to make Mari my life. Mari and my work, and setting up a home. I don't want to hurt you. It has nothing to do with Peter," she repeated.

"Of course not."

"It's because of Mari."

"Yes."

Her head jerked up. "Stop arguing with me!"

Had he given something away in his tone? "Sweet, I haven't any intention of arguing with you." He added, "Right now. Right now there isn't any point in arguing with you about anything, now, is there?"

She closed her eyes wearily. "No."

"You're so tired you can't see straight."

"You have to go home."

"Yes, you said that." He stopped playing with her hair, and to distract her said quietly, "I think you'd better tell me the rest of it, Laura. Like on what grounds did you get the divorce?"

"I . . . *Owen.*"

His fingers were very gently, very quietly unbuttoning her blouse, which wasn't easy. The room was dark, and she persisted in wearing blouses with itty-bitty buttons. "I'm going to give you a back rub. And then put you to bed. No pass. No kisses. No nothing. Hear me? Now, on what grounds did you get the divorce?"

"I don't want a back rub!"

"I don't much care. You're getting one."

Laura stared up at him mutinously as he slipped his palm between her soft skin and the cloth of her blouse. Off one shoulder, then the other. His touch was as impersonal as it was . . . determined. And the look in his dark eyes sent an irrational, foolish tremor up and down her spine. He would have her believe she wanted him to undress her. To be naked in front of him. As vulnerable as a woman can be . . . only with him. "Don't . . . look at me that way. Owen—"

"Just talk, Laura. Stop thinking. Custody of Mari—how was that set up?" He dropped her blouse on the floor.

"You're not listening to me."

"I heard you. You don't want a relationship, and it has nothing to do with Peter. A back rub is not a relationship; a back rub is just a back rub, and you're tired as hell. You also happen to trust me, whether you know it or not. So let's not make too much fuss over nothing."

"I am *not* taking off this skirt."

"Of course you're not. I am." The skirt had an elasticized waistband. He skimmed his fingers inside, sliding it down over her hips, controlling the impulse to linger. Her skin was white and smooth, all shadowed hollows and curves in the darkness. The scent of her was everywhere.

"Owen," Laura said politely, "I'm going to smack you."

It would have been difficult to hit him when she was flat on her stomach on the mattress. One lost a certain amount of fighting momentum, dressed only in panties and bra, when a man's muscled thighs were straddling you. When he leaned over her and stole the pillow from beneath her cheek, she felt the weight of him, the maleness of him.

His fingers pushed aside her hair, then settled in on the knotted muscles at the nape of her neck. *You have to make him leave.* But her body wasn't listening to her head. With each kneading caress, her thighs tensed together and the blood in her veins was turning warm, thick, heated. It was dark, making her near nudity feel less . . . intimate. Or more.

She desperately didn't want him to leave. She just wanted to be twenty again, before she'd met Peter, before sexual feelings and anxiety had become a matched set for her. It wasn't possible to go back. And if Owen had been any kind of . . . gentleman, he'd have left when she asked him to.

But he hadn't. Like a pirate's, his hands possessively marauded her flesh, stealing the bra straps from her shoulders, kneading tense muscles as if they were booty. He stroked her skin as if it were treasure. His thumbs probed each vertebra, turning each into liquid.

"That's my lady," he murmured. "Unhook your bra in front, sweet."

"There's no need to—"

"Or I can," he said smoothly.

There was a moment's silence.

"Owen," Laura said irritably.

There was another moment's silence. Laura unhooked the bra. As fast as she whipped off the wisp of nylon, her body mashed to the mattress as if glued there. She was also in a sudden hurry to talk. "All right. You asked me about the divorce . . ."

As she talked, Owen's hands claimed more and

more territory. Her neck, so vulnerable. The sweet slope of her hips. The sides of her breasts. He listened, but every muscle, every pulse, every nerve, strained with the primal need to take her. To gather her up, lay kisses on every secret place, to cover and claim. To make love to her and make love to her and make love to her. To teach her to abandon her restraint, to coax the sensual Laura into flower, to erase that foolish, foolish fear that she wasn't woman enough.

Instead, he forced himself to listen. ". . . So you had a time with the lawyers."

"Divorce lawyers only want to talk settlements. I didn't want a settlement; I just wanted out, and I wasn't about to tell some stranger about my personal life. I understand that the law is the law, but my marital problem wasn't any of their business."

"Yes." He didn't smile, but for an instant he had a wry suspicion that Laura just might not have made the attorneys' job all that simple.

"The easiest way to get a divorce these days is on grounds of 'irretrievable breakdown of the marriage.' Only my attorneys said I wouldn't find a judge who'd give me a divorce on those grounds— at least not a fast divorce—because I was expecting a child. So I had to find other grounds." Laura closed her eyes. Exhaustion was stealing over her like a black fog. Suddenly, it was all so easy to talk about. Talking muted the rush of yearning evoked by Owen's hands, the flood of wanting that was so disturbing. "I got my fast divorce, Owen, and I got it before Mari was born. Somehow . . . when you're very sure of what you feel, of what's right, of what you want . . . there's always a way."

His hands stilled. "Laura. What did you have to do?" he asked quietly.

"Sue him for infidelity. Ironic, yes? I stood up there and said he'd been unfaithful with other women—and knew very well he'd never touched another woman." Her voice was muffled in the pillow. "The attorney told me I'd need proof. I didn't. The judge was an old codger, half senile, and anyway he couldn't say much once Peter stood up and admitted to having had a number of long . . . affairs."

Owen's hand glided up to her shoulders, his mind recreating that scene in the courtroom. "I thought you told me your ex-husband didn't want the divorce."

"He didn't. But in court, he didn't have a choice because he was afraid I'd blurt out the truth, that he slept with men." Laura's voice took on a weary note. Owen's fingers stole over her scalp, soothing, soothing, soothing. "He didn't want anyone to know. Our friends had no idea, and any hint of his homosexuality would have destroyed his parents. That's why I moved, why I broke contact with all the people I knew. I couldn't answer their questions without either lying or hurting him, so I left." She added quietly, "Yes, I lied in court, Owen. It seemed the only way. I didn't want to destroy Peter, just . . . to get out of his life."

Which sounded, to Owen, very much like Laura. Never to hurt anyone, no matter how badly she'd been hurt. "And custody?"

"The judge wouldn't—or couldn't—rule on the

permanent custody of an unborn child. Temporarily, the baby's simply mine, and Peter has 'reasonable visiting rights.' Later on, we'll have to go back to court and make a more permanent arrangement."

His hands stilled again. "Are you worried about that?"

Laura sighed. "No. Mari is mine. If Peter fights for custody, I'll use his private life against him if I have to." She added fiercely, "I don't want to do that, but I'll do anything to keep Mari."

"I know you would, Laura," he said softly.

She hesitated, her voice becoming more distant. "I haven't . . . got all that settled in my head yet. About his rights, where Mari is concerned. Mari's his daughter, probably the only child he'll ever have. He's a talented man; he can be warm and affectionate and gentle. I have to be fair. In my head, I believe he has the right to spend time with her, to be her father. But in my heart, I seem to have some old-fashioned prejudices, Owen. It's not just his sexual preference. Deep inside, he's a troubled, unhappy man; I don't want that rubbing off on Mari. I don't want confusion in her life. Owen?"

He leaned closer to hear.

"What have you done to me? I feel like one long soggy noodle," she murmured groggily.

He chuckled. "Sleep," he whispered. Long after he'd covered her, he lay next to her on his back in the darkness, his eyes open and his heart thudding in his chest.

Through the long night, he went over and over Laura's story. Laura did what she had to do, a quality Owen respected and loved in her. She hadn't hesitated to lie to get her divorce. She wouldn't hesitate to tell the truth to keep her child. And whatever decision she came to about Peter's custody rights, Owen knew it would be the right one. She was a strong woman, extremely capable of making decisions, willing to travel a rough road if that's what it took to do the right thing.

His lady was also hurt and vulnerable—he was just beginning to understand how much. She'd built a mountain between herself and intimacy ... his lady who smelled like hyacinths, who had a terrible pride about facing problems alone, who'd brought warmth and laughter to his life without even trying.

He was in love with her. In his head, he knew Laura had to be the one to tear down that mountain. In his heart, he wanted to do it for her. Either way, he knew he had to tread carefully.

Laura woke with a start. Sunlight was streaming over her bed as if it were midmorning. A glance at the clock confirmed it was nearly eight o'clock, and a glance at the dented pillow next to her confirmed that she hadn't slept alone.

This just wasn't possible. Mari should have been starving two hours earlier, and as for Owen—he couldn't possibly have spent the night, because she wouldn't have let him. Except that snapshot memories darted through her mind like the click of a camera. Quick images of telling him her whole life story, then of Owen bringing the baby to nurse in the middle of the night. Of falling asleep and finding the baby gone. Of reaching out in the wee hours of the morning, of being enfolded in warm, strong arms, of feeling his palm cup her breast, of feeling his thighs spooned against hers... Cheeks flushed, she bolted from the bed, whipped on an ivory cotton sundress, and hurried down the hall.

The baby's room was empty. So was the bathroom. So were the hall, stairs, living room, kitchen... Heart thudding, she threw open the back door, and abruptly collapsed in relief against the doorjamb.

Owen was stretched out on a chaise lounge on the deck, barefoot. The baby was lying on her back on his stomach. Both appeared to be reading the business section of the newspaper, and Owen had a cup of coffee next to him. "Morning, lazybones."

So bright, so innocuously cheerful. Laura was highly tempted to pick him up and throw him into the nearest body of water—but he was a little heavy, and there wasn't a body of water handy. And unfortunately, at that exact moment, she had the terrible feeling that her heart was already dangerously attached to the man. Partly because of the way Mari looked in his arms. And the way he parted his hair. And his nose. *Laura.* She tried to make her voice sound lethally polite. "I don't believe it's this late." *Or that you're still here* was understood.

Owen's eyes took a lazy path from her bare feet to the soft ivory sundress to the tousled hair curling on her shoulders. En route, he noted without surprise the fire in her turquoise eyes. He'd known the peaceful interlude couldn't last. Sleeping, Laura had proved wonderfully moldable, curling around him like a temptress. He'd known better than to expect such pliability once she woke.

Folding the paper, he stood up, swinging the baby to his shoulder. "I'll make breakfast while you feed her."

"No," Laura said swiftly. "I'll feed her, then make breakfast. *You*—sit."

The man didn't have an ounce of obedience in him. By the time she'd nursed Mari, brushed her teeth, and restored a little order to her hair, Owen was humming over a frying pan of scrambled eggs. One would think nothing had happened the night before. One would think that he hadn't spent the night in her bed, that Peter had never been there, that Owen hadn't very clearly been told she wasn't in the market for a man in her kitchen.

"We have something to discuss," she said firmly as she sat down to an overflowing breakfast plate.

"Shoot."

"You're in the habit," she started tactfully, "of getting your own way."

"I know." He sounded apologetic.

"You're not exactly arrogant, but you're right on the borderline. I mean, you walk all over people if they let you."

Owen tried hard to look like an innocent man holding a baby. He nodded. "I've been accused of this before."

"That baby is not going to protect you, Owen."

"I thought it was worth a try."

"No. And I did *not* invite you to spend the night."

"I know."

"And if you think I'm incapable of kicking my own ex-husband out of my own house, you're mistaken."

"I knew you'd be mad about that," he agreed, and added mildly, "Want to see a movie tonight?"

"And do what with Mari? No. And don't stray from the subject."

"Sorry."

"You are *not* sorry about anything." Laura put down her fork and folded her arms. Getting mad was proving tougher than it should be. For openers, it was difficult to act self-righteous around a man you'd snuggled with all night, and for closers, he clearly wasn't paying attention. He was chucking Mari under the chin, and the baby was giggling. *"Owen."*

His head whipped and he threw her a disarming smile. "I'm listening, honestly."

"The problem is that you have nothing to do," she announced severely. "You're at loose ends, trying to stay away from work for a time. So you saw a lady in a little distress and found yourself a cause. I've been thinking about this—"

"Want some coffee?" he interrupted politely.

"No, thank you." She frowned, distracted, and then picked up the thread again. "I mean, look, Owen. It's obvious I'm not the kind of woman you'd normally be attracted to." She motioned to her hair. "Unstyled and uncut, four months now."

He looked where the sun was gilding a streak of soft hair near her temples.

She motioned to her face. "No makeup."

He noted the creamy softness of her skin. Just one night of decent sleep had erased the fragile hollows beneath her eyes.

"No style." She motioned to the simple sundress, then to her stomach. "Paunchy."

He loved her in ivory and wondered vaguely when she was going to get over her sensitivity about her stomach which was flatter than most women's anyway.

"*So...*" Laura repeated firmly, "you're not here because you're attracted to me, Owen. Look, maybe I've sent you the wrong signals about needing someone. You have this protective nature—"

"I know you didn't spend the whole night thinking this stuff up, because you slept like a log," Owen said mildly. "I really think you need a cup of coffee."

"I don't *want* a cup of coffee."

"Sure?"

She sighed as he gently put a steaming mug in front of her. Owen studied her, his dark eyes impassive. When she took the first sip, it was his turn.

"You're right about everything," he said magnanimously, and watched her eyes blink wide open. "We couldn't possibly have a case of attraction going for us. I mean, look at me." He motioned to his thick mane of hair. "I know it looks okay now, but you probably guessed. At sixty-five, the men in our family start going bald." He motioned to his chin. "My mother calls this a bulldog chin." He motioned down and down again. "Bony knees. Big feet. Hairy le—"

"*Owen.*" He was a mean mimic. And she could

feel a most irrational smile forming on her lips.

"So you couldn't possibly be attracted to me, now, could you, sweet?"

"I didn't say that," Laura said abruptly, and then frowned. Owen was . . . twisting things.

Owen said softly, "Laura, he was one man, a man with a unique set of problems that he tried to lay on you. How long are you going to make yourself pay for his problems? Wake up, honey. I love you, and I think you're damn close to loving me. And I don't think it's caring or loving that you're afraid of—but the intimate physical side of a relationship. Sex can wait. You'll trust that it's right in time." He glanced around. "I'll do the dishes."

"*I'll* do the dishes." Laura leaped to her feet, grabbing the plates. "Owen, you're wrong. I'm not afraid of . . . anything. You're *dead* wrong. My dad is a geologist; we traveled all over the world. I was never afraid of starting over, making new friends, settling in new places. It took courage to demand a divorce when I was two months pregnant. Moving here, where I knew no one, having the baby alone— no one can accuse me of not having courage!"

Owen rinsed out a cup and set it in the dishwasher, holding Mari at the same time. "You are," he agreed lightly, "a very courageous lady. Want the margarine in the fridge?"

"No. Yes." Laura flipped back her hair, feeling thoroughly unnerved. Thoroughly distracted, she rinsed the rest of the dishes and slipped them in the dishwasher. *I love you, and I think you're damn close to loving me.*

Did she? Did she love the man who was busy carrying her baby around, putting the bread in the wrong place, and stealing a cookie from the box directly after breakfast? The man who never coated honesty with sugar or champagne? The man she'd trusted enough to tell her story to the night before?

Yes.

And for a time she wanted to just be alone and absorb the reality of loving him. Instead, he was bringing her an egg-caked frying pan to scour and leaning over her while she did it, the baby kicking on his shoulder and his voice as soothing as silk in water. "So we're just going to spend time together for a while. No-pressure time, okay?"

"No." She attacked the pan with a vengeance.

"I always leave the egg pan on the counter to soak."

"You would—being male," she said teasingly.

His tone changed from casual to gruff and gravelly. "And a male you can kick out any time, Laura. If I've misunderstood how you feel . . ."

His comment seemed to linger in the air. Laura lifted the clean pan out of the sudsy water and rinsed it. Her counters needed wiping; there was a fingerprint on a cupboard, then the stove . . . She was suddenly very busy. Only a few moments later, there was nothing left to do.

She slipped her hands into the pockets of her sundress and turned to face him. "No. You haven't misunderstood anything," she said softly. "But I can't promise you anything either, Owen. Maybe I am afraid . . . of a physical relationship." She took a breath. "I also know it isn't fair to ask you to wait while I sort out that part of my life."

"Fair?" he chided. He took two steps forward, close enough to brush her cheek tenderly with his hand. "It takes two to be fair, Laura. You've been hurt . . . and I've been pushing you faster than you wanted to go. We'll wait until you're ready."

"And if that's never?"

He smiled. *"Never's* a silly word, sweet."

She looked at him searchingly. The man said he loved her, and if the look in his eyes was anything to go by, he meant it. He also had all but said he was willing to settle for a platonic relationship for now . . . but she knew better.

Owen was a virile man, a sensual man, and he wanted her. She wanted him just as much, but expressing that desire—she wasn't sure if she could, when it meant the risk of failing him as a woman. For now, it wasn't a problem. For now, she had those convenient stitches she kept teasing him with.

But those would heal. And if she'd learned nothing else from her marriage with Peter, she'd learned that two people have to give and need and want in the same way. Laura couldn't take love and caring from Owen without offering them equally in return.

- 7 -

LAURA OPENED THE refrigerator and glared at the treasure trove of chocolates. Jaws clamped together, she closed the refrigerator and stalked back to her dining room–*cum* office.

Mari was six weeks old today; Laura's stomach was finally flat again, and there was no way she was going to blow it by bingeing on chocolates. If alcoholics and chain smokers could kick their habits, so could she.

She muttered one brisk "Damn Owen," and collapsed in the chair behind her desk. Work was stacked everywhere, ready to distract her. A Queen Anne tiger-maple spice box needed shipping. She was in the middle of a search for a presidential portrait clock with an Aaron Willard label. There was a letter by the phone promising her a sizable commission if she could find a set of dram cups for a collector of antique sterling wine tasters. She started shuffling paper.

A half-hour later, she bolted from the chair, stalked to the refrigerator, removed an infinitely small, sweet cherry coated with white chocolate, and defiantly popped it into her mouth.

The taste was enough to make her lean weakly against the wall in delirious pleasure. Lord, it was good. Owen made *wonderful* chocolates.

Owen was also the reason her desk was piled too high with more work than she could possibly handle. Laura listened at the stairs for Mari's wake-up-from-nap cry, heard nothing, and determinedly returned to work. Picking up the phone, she flicked an imaginary piece of lint from her pink cotton skirt and forced herself to concentrate on business.

Or *tried* to concentrate on business. The taste of chocolate lingered on her tongue. After three weeks of watching them accumulate on her shelf, surely she deserved one fall off the chocoholic wagon? It wasn't as if she really believed there was a natural aphrodisiac in Owen's candy.

And even if there were, depriving herself had successfully made her feel like a martyr . . . but hadn't helped her in the least with getting Owen off her mind.

It was his fault. For two weeks, he'd just been around, like the teasing presence of something she couldn't have, like a craving for something she knew was dangerous.

Take Saturday, for instance. She'd patiently explained to him why they couldn't take Mari to a movie—filmgoers didn't appreciate disturbing influences like screaming infants. Only Mari hadn't disturbed anyone. She'd gurgled contentedly from Owen's lap in the darkness and appeared enthralled by the love scenes. Laura had also been enthralled by the love scenes. Owen had munched on popcorn.

And then on Wednesday, she'd voted for McDonald's, and been outvoted in favor of a restaurant with candles and damask tablecloths and wine and the most delectable prime rib . . . Owen should have known better. Mari never stayed good that long at mealtime. Only Mari had been an angel, perched on her infant seat next to the table, and Owen had looked delectable in his charcoal suit, with his sleepy gray eyes and husky voice.

And there were other times. He was always showing up for breakfast. Twice he'd shown up after a long day in New York only to fall asleep on her couch.

His scotch had found its way into her cupboard.

He'd gone with her to buy a new car and acted like a husband, all picky and difficult about details and price and color. He wanted her to buy a high-powered van that cost a fortune. Instead, she'd bought a used Volvo.

On Tuesday, she'd taken Mari to Paige's. Owen had been waiting as if the prospect of a grocery-store trip delighted him. Never again. Shopping had taken her twice as long as it should have; he was a terrible impulse buyer.

He'd taken up chess. In a sense. He'd bought a chess set and brought it to the house and expected her to teach him how to play. Then beat her, the skunk.

When he was beat from a tough day, occasionally he brought home a domineering attitude. Once reasoning failed, she tried spilling a glass of lemonade on his pants. Any sane man would have walked out the door right then and there, but Owen had burst out laughing and the evening had ended with a serious talk about men who took charge too often . . . and about men who were trying to learn tolerance and patience.

And Mari. Mari had smiled, her first one that Laura was absolutely positive wasn't gas. Owen was there.

Owen had been there almost every day for two weeks. He hadn't always been on his best behavior, but he never played games. Trust was building, whether Laura wanted it to or not. Trust, caring, affection, laughter, love . . . and he'd sidestepped every possible chance to touch her. He was clearly leaving that completely up to her.

Work, she reminded herself, picking up the list of estates that might have wine tasters for sale, and frowned. She was supposed to be concentrating on presidential clocks.

"*Exactly* where I was afraid I'd find you."

Laura's head jerked up in surprise and pleasure. Damn the man. She was increasingly aware that even the look of him was enough to turn her on, and neither overwork nor chocolates helped.

His pin-striped suit wasn't her favorite; it made him look formidable and austere when she knew he was gentle and humorous. Regardless, the suit fit his whipcord-lean frame perfectly; he was standing with that knee-forward masculine stance she was beginning to find so familiar ... and only belatedly did she note the steadfast glare in his charcoal eyes.

"I forgot something?" she guessed guiltily.

"The doctor. I told you I'd be back to watch Mari while you went to the doctor." He added, "This is the second appointment you've tried to wiggle out of this week."

"The doctor," she echoed glumly. "I completely—"

"Forgot." Owen moved forward swiftly, stealing the paper from her one hand, the ballpoint pen from the other. "That was your excuse two days ago when you canceled. Not this time, Laura."

His eyes swept lazily over her pale pink ribboned top, her untidy knot of light brown hair, her slim, bare legs. She flushed, for no reason. For two weeks, his hands had behaved themselves. His eyes just didn't always.

Laura was well aware of what was going on. Owen was waiting for her to cross mountains she just couldn't cross.

But she wanted to. Increasingly, she desperately wanted to. "Owen, I can't..." She hesitated. "Go to the doctor, I mean. Mari's still napping, and if I leave now she'll wake up and be hungry—"

"So you'd better be on your way in a hurry," Owen interrupted calmly.

"I'm not dressed for the doctor."

"You don't dress for the doctor. You undress for him."

"Her," she corrected absently. "My obstetrician is a her. And anyway, I'm perfectly healthy. The whole thing is nonsense. I have a thousand things to do; I've seen enough doctors in the last few months to support the AMA."

"Primarily for Mari. Now it's your turn. And tell the doc about the long hours you've been putting in lately." He disappeared and returned seconds later with her sandals dangling from one finger.

Laura paused. "You know," she said conversationally, "I thought we'd worked this bossy streak out of you in the last few weeks."

Owen chuckled, but the glance he sent Laura was thoughtful. Sun flickered on the delicate slant of her cheekbones, highlighting the translucent quality of her skin. She was so beautiful . . . and so darned close to worrying herself ill. Over something she shouldn't be worried about at all. "I'd rather you took my car than the rattletrap you bought," he offered, and firmly, gently reached out to steal her hand.

"Owen . . ." He seemed to be dragging her toward the door. And the feel of his firm, strong fingers over hers was the touch of diamonds, producing brilliant, crystallike sensations that made her pulse leap.

"Don't worry about Mari. Out you go, now." He

opened the door and playfully patted her through it.

On the other side of the screen, Laura perched with her hands on her hips, shoes still dangling from her fingers. "Could I at least have my purse?" she asked dryly.

"Yes." He shook a finger at her. "I'll get it. *Don't* come back inside."

She had her shoes on by the time he slipped her purse through a narrow opening in the screen. Laughing, Laura grabbed it. "I hope Mari's terrible for you. I hope she gives you fits. I hope she wears you out. I hope—"

Owen waved her off, then stood there, his smile fading. He badly needed to know what the doctor had to say. After spending every spare moment with her over the last few weeks, he felt love growing inside him like an insatiable wonder. And Laura, the way she brightened when he walked in, her laughter, her teasing . . . he knew what she felt. If not as deep as his own, he was nevertheless increasingly certain that she felt love for him, too.

And lately she was finding excuses to touch him. The slight adjustment of a tie that didn't need straightening. Her hand slipped through his when they walked. The brush of fingers on his shoulders, the starkness of wanting in her eyes the night they'd watched the stars . . . it was all there. The chemistry of desire.

Owen had waited, and was prepared to wait a great deal longer for her to initiate a change in their relationship, but he was increasingly aware that she wasn't going to. He guessed that she had built up a fear that was way out of proportion. She was overworking, taking on extra projects when she'd originally planned to accept only a few commitments this soon after the baby. And she was worrying, not sleeping nights. She'd be eating dinner, then look up at him, then start talking a mile a minute and pick at her food.

Perhaps she didn't feel the desire as strongly as he did. Perhaps he just wanted her to.

He did know that they couldn't go on like this much longer. Laura was hurting more, not less.

"Owen? Mari?" Laura rushed through the door with an expectant smile. A light was on in her living room, but there was no sign of life. Mari's diaper bag was gone from its usual spot near the door.

She found a note propped against her lighthouse clock, and shook her head with a wry grin. The bold scrawl stated simply that Mari had been in no mood to wait peacefully for her mother. Owen had drawn a small map at the bottom of the page.

Owen's place? Obviously, it had to be. For weeks, she'd wondered what his home looked like, but a small crease dented her brow as she hurried back to her car. By now, Mari was undoubtedly roaring hungry and giving Owen fits.

He didn't live far away, but it took her a long time and a little backtracking to find the winding country road hidden in a narrow hollow between wooded hills. A quarter-mile of shade, then a blast of late afternoon sun, and she stepped out of her car, ready to rush pell-mell into the house. Then she paused for a moment, bemused.

Somehow, she'd expected Owen to have an ultramodern place. She couldn't have been more wrong. It was a rumbling Norman-style house with a turreted stucco, wood, and brick exterior. The circular driveway led to an imposing entrance, and the well-landscaped grounds were softened by spreading yews and flowering rhododendron. To one side, she could see a wrought-iron balcony overlooking a long slope of lawn that descended into a steep wood.

"Like it?"

"Love it!" Laura pivoted on her heel. Owen was standing in the doorway with a hungry, wailing Mari in his arms. His suit coat and tie were gone, his shirtsleeves rolled up. One *did* have the impression that a twelve-pound package of trouble had put one controlled, competent businessman through the mill. She rushed forward guiltily. "Darn it, I'm sorry Owen. I didn't mean to be so long—"

"No problem."

"She's given you a terrible time?" Mari, instead of calming down for her mother, let out an even more pitiful yell when Laura cradled her.

"Relax. She's been fine until about ten minutes ago, when she decided she wanted dinner and no more excuses."

"Only ten minutes ago? But I thought that was why you left my place, because she was so restless . . . ?" Laura turned to give him a quizzical look, but the baby was making it very clear she was violently unhappy. Laura hugged her lovingly. Such a temper! She had only a moment's glimpse of the slate floor in the entranceway, before Owen led her down three steps to a sunken living room.

"I'll bring something to drink," Owen said from behind them, and left the room.

Unnerved by Mari's increasingly piercing cries, Laura plopped into the nearest seat—an oversized gold sofa—and hurriedly unbuttoned her blouse. The baby stopped wailing the instant she discovered dinner. "I wasn't even a half-hour late," Laura scolded softly, her finger stroking her daughter's cheek. "You'd think I'd deserted you for life."

Her eyes scanned the room curiously, from its huge stone fireplace and French doors to the luxurious Oriental rug. The moldings and floor were oak; his colors a muted gold and very dark blue. Two thick, overstuffed couches; Cezanne prints; a scrolled bar . . . it was a man's room, rich in color and comforts, a distinctly restful haven.

"Here we go . . ."

"Oh . . ." Laura flushed, aware she hadn't taken the time to search out a baby blanket—or anything else—to cover herself with. Owen's eyes were on hers, though, not below, and he extended a wineglass to her.

"So . . . what did the doctor say?"

She took a small sip of wine, then set down the glass. "I love the room, and the outside, Owen. How long have you had the house?"

Owen lowered himself on the matching couch opposite her, stretching out his legs, a dry smile on his lips. So they weren't going to discuss her visit to the doctor. "I bought the house three years ago— you hungry?"

She shook her head. "I've got meat defrosting on the counter at home."

"No, you haven't. I put it back in the refrigerator for you. Thought you might like to celebrate tonight."

"Celebrate?"

"It feels like that kind of night, doesn't it?"

Her eyebrows lifted like delicate wings. "Am I missing something? Did the Yankees win a game by some miracle? Has peace been declared in the Middle East? Has a bumper crop of cocoa beans just been announced?"

He chuckled and toasted her with his glass. "I thought we'd celebrate . . . platonic relationships." Lazily, he stood up and bent over Mari, his hair so close Laura could touch it, his clean-shaven cheek so near she could catch a vague whiff of his shaving cream. "Isn't she beautiful?" he commented.

Laura refrained from plastering her hand over her bare breast, but the pulse in her throat suddenly went haywire. "Particularly when she's quiet?"

Coal-dark eyes shifted up to hers. "Whether she's quiet, or furious, or determined to get her own way . . . she's still beautiful."

She assured herself he was talking about Mari. If Owen would just stop looking at her . . . "Could I take a quick tour of the house?"

He paused to consider, as if this were the toughest decision he'd had to make in years. "No fair opening closets—the cleaning lady doesn't do closets."

She chuckled, feeling at ease when his eyes returned to neutral territory.

"And there's one door upstairs that's closed—I'd like to show you that room another time."

She lifted Mari to her shoulder, turning away to button her blouse. "You can't throw out a teaser like that and expect me not to be curious."

"I'll take the baby. You go poke around and be nosy—but I guarantee I'll know if you put one fingertip on that closed door upstairs."

With her hands stuffed in her pockets, she poked around and was nosy. Downstairs, he had a wonderful country kitchen with oak cabinets and a skylight. Beyond was a dining room, then a wonderfully bright solarium, and a long den with a computer at one end and a billiard table at the other, the balls all set up for a break. So he liked a game of pool, did he?

She wandered upstairs, poked her head into a spare bedroom, a bath, another bedroom, and out of nowhere craved a chocolate. She needed one. *I thought we'd celebrate . . . platonic relationships.*

Sands were shifting beneath her. For two weeks, she'd been safe, and suddenly she knew she wasn't.

She paused at the doorway to a third bedroom. Covers had been laid back on the twin bed, and turned-around chairs made a makeshift crib for Mari. The baby's diaper bag spilled over with a dozen sleepers, and a huge box of disposable diapers stood in one corner. Owen had packed as if preparing the baby for a long trip, not a few hours' visit.

A small pulse in her throat decided to beat double time as she wandered to the next door. Owen's bedroom. The carpet was a pewter gray, not unlike the color of his eyes. A small corner fireplace with a black marble hearth, a dozen logs stacked neatly next to it. His spread was a muted spray of burnt orange and gray, unusual colors together. They worked somehow.

It was a big bed. There was no TV set for entertainment, not in this bedroom. She wandered in. Fading sunlight made a soft yellow halo around the balcony window. On a chair was a small case—Laura recognized it and frowned. Inside the case were silky white pants, a fragile mauve blouse, a zippered makeup kit, a toothbrush. All hers.

The pulse in her throat suddenly hammered out a heavy-metal rhythm. More disturbing than finding her things was discovering that she wanted them there. In his room. By his bed.

She wandered back out and paused in front of the last door before she headed downstairs again. His closed door. Her hand just touched the knob.

"Don't you dare!" Owen growled up the stairs.

"I wasn't," she protested, her tone all innocence, and immediately ran to the top of the stairs. He was standing at the bottom carrying the baby football style, his dark eyes glinting up at her. "Lord. Don't you have any trust in womankind?"

"You were going to peek."

"I was not." She swept down the stairs, giving him an offended look, ruined by his knowing grin waiting for her at the bottom. She sighed. "It's your own fault. Darn it, I respect your privacy—anyone's privacy. I have *never* intruded on anyone's privacy. But you sort of—"

"Tantalized your curiosity?" He tch-tched, handed her the baby, and moved toward the kitchen. "Let me tantalize it a little more. Come see what's for dinner."

She saw, and momentarily forgot about everything upstairs.

A champagne bottle, tucked into an ice bucket, was on the kitchen table. A huge pot of boiling water was bubbling on the stove. And she stared, mesmerized, at the two lobsters crawling around in his sink.

He took one look at her and knew things were not going to go smoothly.

"Laura. You told me you loved lobster."

"I do."

"They're best fresh."

"I'm sure they are." She smiled at him brilliantly, the color completely drained from her face. "They're so . . . alive, aren't they?"

He sighed. "Laura, I can't very well take them back to the store."

"I wasn't asking you to. I would never have asked you to. Look, I'll get over it."

He took them back to the store, and returned with Big Macs. They washed down the hamburgers with champagne, and neither of them could seem to stop laughing. The baby sat on Laura's lap, spending most of her time trying to make her toe reach her mouth.

Later, Mari sat in her infant seat at the counter,

where she supervised a few glasses being washed. After that, she watched the evening news, perched on Owen's stomach, and watched her mother watch Owen watch her mother as if Mari weren't there at all. The baby yawned, bored with this nonsense.

"You're sure you're not irritated about the lobsters?" Laura questioned.

"You know I'm not." Owen switched off the news, which neither of them had been paying attention to anyway, and readjusted the couch pillow behind his head. "I should have expected you to react that way."

"What way?"

"Softhearted. I hate to tell you this, love, but you're really Silly Putty."

"Would *you* like to die in a vat of boiling water?" she demanded.

He chuckled. "How would you like to see a vat of liquid chocolate tomorrow?"

"Pardon?"

"Come with me to Reesling's. Want to see how chocolates are made?"

She opened one eye. Flopped on the couch across from him—one glass of champagne inevitably made mush of her bones—she viewed Owen through a spray of thick lashes. "Yes and no."

"Sounds like a Laura-like answer to me."

"Yes, I would *love* to see your chocolates."

"And no?"

"And exactly why are my things upstairs in your bedroom?" Her tone was casual. Deliberately casual.

Owen offered the baby his thumb. Mari immediately grasped it and swung it toward her gums. "I was hoping you'd spend the night."

"Were you?"

"You and I," he said gently, "are both tired of playing it platonic, sweet. And I believe you would have found some way to tell me immediately if your stitches weren't out yet—if the doctor hadn't given you a completely clean bill of health."

She stared at a fascinating spot in his ceiling. "You said—you promised—you'd be patient."

"My patience isn't the problem. You are. If you need a year to think, love, I'll give you that year, but there's a difference between thinking and stalling. Now, at this point you've got shadows under your eyes, and you've buried yourself under a pile of work, trying to pretend something isn't there that is."

"Owen—"

"We've tried it your way. Now we're going to try it mine," he said mildly.

She turned to look at him. At the man who'd returned the lobsters and brought back Big Macs for her. At the man who hadn't laid a finger on her in two weeks. At the man who could have tried to seduce her after a few more glasses of champagne, but instead insisted on being honest. At the man holding her baby on his stomach and looking at her with stark, raw desire.

"No," she said hesitantly.

"Yes."

"We've been doing fine—"

"The first time," he said gently, "may be rough. You're scared as hell. I'm not sure I understand why, but I know your fear has to do with your ex. We'll work that out, Laura."

"Owen—"

The baby let out one sharp wail, irritated at being ignored.

"I can't," Laura said softly. "I *can't*, Owen."

Owen sat up and lifted the baby in his arms. "You want a bath, don't you, Mari? And your mother needs a little laughter. You'd think I'd just told her we were going to shoot the Snake River rapids without a raft, and here all I want to do is make love to her." He shook his head despairingly, looking down at the baby. Behind him, his hand reached out for Laura's. "Upstairs, ladies. One thing at a time."

- 8 -

"LAURA, I HATE to be the one to tell you this, but your daughter has one small problem."

"Yes?"

"She thinks she's a porpoise."

From across the huge circular tub, Laura bent an elbow on the porcelain edge and cupped her chin in her palm. Her eyes danced over to Owen. "Are you ready to cry uncle yet?"

"Of course I'm not crying uncle. One grown man should be able to handle the bathing of one small infa—She splashed me!" he said indignantly. He raised a winsome grin. "A few short years from now, we can enter her in the Olympics. Freestyle, of course. Fast, but no discipline. In the meantime, have you had lifeguard training?"

"Think I'm going to need it?"

"It's a possibility—Dammit, she's as slippery as a greased pig." Abruptly, he bent over a vigorously kicking Mari. "I apologize for calling you a greased pig, princess."

Chuckling, Laura rocked back on her heels and again surveyed Owen's "secret room." The huge bathroom was divided into two parts by a glass door. The front section was a luxurious blend of black marble and brass, with lots of mirrors and man-size towels and thick pile carpeting.

Beyond the glass door was what Owen called a "climate room." Laura realized that was a euphemism for a hedonist's dream. The black marble tub was circular and large enough for three people. Recessed lighting reflected off smooth ebony tiles, streaked with gold. Behind Owen's head was a control panel. A punch of a button ordered up music. At the touch of another button, the scents of a rain forest filled the air with the earthy smell of wet leaves and fresh, warm breezes. A push of another button produced rain. Tropical rain, drizzling down like a warm, wet whisper.

Her gaze wandered back to Owen. Foolishly, he was still wearing his good shirt—which was soaked now. A lock of dark hair hung rakishly over his forehead, which was also good and wet. A rivulet of water was ribboning down his cheek, and Laura watched the play of emotions on his face as he bathed the baby—amusement, frustration, surprise, delight, and even pride. The bond between man and infant was already strong.

That tug of laughter, the caring he showed for Mari, the honesty of the man—dammit, she loved him.

But the blatantly sensual room also unnerved her. It was a playground for the uninhibited, and every time she met Owen's gaze, she saw the steady, insistent male promises in his gray eyes. He wasn't pressing her . . . but she knew something was coming.

"Uncle! Uncle, uncle, uncle—"

"I get the message!" Laura held out a velour towel toward Mari, who protested being taken from the water with a sleepy wail. "You lasted longer than I thought you would," Laura teased Owen.

"Thank you." Owen used a towel to dry his hair. "I'm soaked."

"I noticed."

"Bathing babies is obviously not a spectator sport." Behind her, Owen handed down Mari's sleeper and diaper.

"Thanks. Owen?" Having been fed and bathed, Mari decided she wanted instant sleep, making it difficult for Laura to wiggle her into the summertime sleeper. She smiled, unable to resist planting a kiss on her daughter's cheek. "Did you put this bathroom in yourself?"

"Believe it or not, this room was here when I moved. A little old woman owned this house before me. She was about five feet two, two hundred pounds. The first time I saw the room, I figured she must have had one hell of a fantasy life."

Laura chuckled, then sobered quickly. Owen

crouched down beside her, close enough to brush her arm. Her heart set up a triphammer beat. He'd removed his wet shirt, and his chest was bare. Bare, warm, and vibrantly male. "I'll take the baby and put her to bed," he said casually. "Then it's our turn to take a bath. Sound good?"

She hesitated, hoping the cotton wool in her throat would dissolve. He wasn't asking her simply to take a bath with him; he wanted to make love to her. She knew that all she had to do was say no. Someone else's voice murmured yes, and then far too swiftly, the baby was stolen from her arms.

Sitting on the thickly carpeted floor, she drew her knees up and wrapped her arms around them as she waited for Owen to return. She wished suddenly that she had had other men before Peter. A hundred affairs or a dozen one-night stands, it didn't matter. Any experience that might have lessened the well of dread in the pit of her stomach. But her marriage to Peter hadn't prepared her for lovemaking, only for rejection. Every time she'd let go that secret well of sensuality in herself, Peter had pushed her away, appalled at her show of passion. Every time she'd initiated a caress, he'd made her feel ashamed. In her head, she knew it would be different with Owen, but in her heart, she was so afraid.

Owen carried the baby into the spare room where he'd fashioned the makeshift crib. Mari was yawning, but the minute Owen laid her down, she opened bright blue eyes and blinked. *Don't you dare, little one.*

He covered her with a soft cotton blanket and bent down to press a kiss on the crown of her head. "Listen, princess," he whispered. "Tonight, you sleep hard, understand? I hate to introduce you to bribery this early in life, but I'm willing to talk furs, Porsches, and trips to Europe when you're sixteen—as long as you sleep tonight. Agreed?"

Mari snuggled to her blanket, her eyes closing.

Owen switched out the light.

Laura hadn't moved before he was back in the doorway, his body a rough outline against the night. He could have been a thief, a pirate in the dark; he stood so still for a moment. And then he moved forward, a tall bare-chested man with golden skin and hooded silvery eyes. "Foolish one," he murmured gently. "Nothing's going to happen that you don't want to, Laura. Don't you know that?"

"Yes." She smiled suddenly, meaning it. And then started unbuttoning her blouse as he flicked the faucets on full to fill up the bath. He was undressed and in the water before she'd dropped her blouse to the floor, and her fingers started fumbling suddenly, aware he was watching her.

"Want help?" he asked teasingly.

She shook her head and wished he'd help ... except that she knew he didn't want to. He wanted her to come to him. He wanted her yes loud and clear and honest. And he had that yes, but her eyes lowered as she slipped off her bra, then reached for the buttons of her skirt.

"Hurry."

Her head whipped up for that sudden urgent whisper from Owen. She peeled off the skirt, pushed down the panties, and stepped out of them, and she couldn't stop looking at his eyes, her face pale. *This is all there is, you know. One imperfect woman, stretch marks, inhibitions, and all. If you were expecting Lolita . . .*

The water was warm and infinitely soothing as she stepped over the side and crouched down, facing him, not touching. Her chin was tilted up with bravado, her voice a little huskier than it should have been. "Feels . . . wonderful."

"It does," Owen agreed. With his arms stretched out along the sides of the tub, he relaxed, regarding her with a winsome smile. Then his smile died, and his eyes darkened just like coals turned over to show their fire side.

Laura had been careful to keep her eyes properly averted. Before. When his body had been in shadow and she'd been busy removing her clothes.

Not now. There was nothing to keep her from looking now. He was so very much a man. Water glistened in the fur on his chest, slid down his sinewed shoulders. His skin was all dark gold, his legs long and strong, and in water, his arousal was magnified. The arousal she'd been pretending she hadn't seen. And his dark eyes shone with fierce, male, pagan lights, craving the pale flesh they wandered over. "You're beautiful, love. Even more beautiful than I imagined. Close your eyes for me?"

When she obeyed, Owen reached behind him for the buttons on the control panel. The bright light

over the tub softened to the whispered blue of twi-
light. An infinitely warm breeze brushed her skin.
The murmur of music seemed to come from far
away, faint and seductive and soothing.

She relaxed a little. When he reached out to pull
her close to him, she tensed again, but only for a
moment. He settled her between his thighs, her back
to his chest, and it was Laura who drew his arms
around her, Laura who invited that tight possessive
hold under her breasts. He needed her to do that.
He had to be absolutely sure that her nervousness
was not unwillingness.

His lips started a trail at the crown of her head
and wandered to her cheek. Beneath his palm, he
could hear her heart beating, beating, beating. Her
breasts were full and white and firm, with a satin
flush from the glow of light on water. If he moved
a finger, he could touch them. He didn't. "You know
what I want to do to you, don't you?"

Warm water lapped around her bare skin; she was
conscious of the music and the soft light and the
texture of that silky summer breeze. Yet she felt
surrounded by Owen, by the look of his darker skin
in the water next to hers, by the feel of the damp
hair on his chest against her spine, by the secure
hold of his arms. By his wanting. She could feel,
sense, breathe, inhale . . . his wanting.

And his voice continued to woo, to seduce. "I
want to kiss you naked, sweet. I want to feel your
belly against mine and your breasts grow heavy in
my hands. I want to bury myself inside you, with
your legs wrapped around me. I want to hear you

cry out, with my name on your lips, Laura. *Mine*. You're not going to have time to think about anything else, to worry about how it was with anyone else..."

"Owen..." She leaned her head back. His eyes were a cool, watching silver. A mist clouded her own. *Keep control,* warned her head. But his words had made pictures that sent a fierce, sharp, desperate ache shooting through her body.

"You like my secret room?"

"Yes."

"Are you sure?" His breath whispered over her throat.

She was trying hard to concentrate on the question. Or on reading the odd catch in his voice. Both were difficult to think about when his lips were distracting her, making soft forays down the side of her neck. "Your room is beautiful." Was that her voice, sounding as if she'd been running a long distance? "But it doesn't matter, Owen."

He breathed out a gruff, "I agree." He sounded oddly relieved, but before she had the chance to interpret the thought, he was surging up from the water, raising her with him, water splashing around them. His movements were lithe and sure, and so damned fast.

He enfolded her in a huge dark towel and quickly dried her, not very well. She was still damp when he tossed aside the towel and kissed her, once, then again and again, each one harder, more demanding than the last.

Keep control, the little voices roared in her ears.

But her head tilted back, absorbing the pressure of his mouth. He gave her no choice. Lightning streaked through her bloodstream, a tense bright streak of incredible power. The mat of his chest, his muscular thighs, his smooth shoulders, his arousal . . . her softness yielded to the bold, warm length of him. Not a choice but an instinct.

His head lifted, his eyes searing hers. "The first time, I thought . . . in water. Darkness and music and water, all soft and easy for you. Or champagne and firelight." He shook his head. "That's not the way. You don't need props, Laura, and neither do I. All I want is you, just you, and a damned hard mattress."

God, he was wild. Desire, raw and urgent, tightened his body against hers. She could taste hunger in his mouth, an intimate, gnawing hunger that matched something long-buried in her. The hall was a blur, the air suddenly cool on her bare skin. *Keep control,* shouted those voices again, but in his room there were only cool, smooth sheets and Owen lying down beside her. Devil fingers cupped her breasts, lifted them to his tongue, the graze of his teeth.

His leg stole between her thighs, anchoring her, leaving her no room to move, no space where she couldn't feel the weight of him, the wanting of him. Hours before, she'd put on perfume; the scent came back now, as her flesh warmed under his hands and tongue. *Keep control . . .*

If he would just go faster . . . but suddenly he switched to an infinitely slow pace. A thin cry escaped her lips when his mouth sucked at her nipple.

His hand smoothed down to the soft fur guarding the tender spot between her legs, and her limbs convulsed around him.

She felt his lips on her cheeks, in her hair. He coaxed forth her response, not with softness but with fire. The wanton flame inside her grew brighter, sneaking around emotional doors she'd thought locked. She wanted his skin, naked, hot. She wanted his hands on her. She wanted him to be just as fierce and willful and terrifying a lover as he was.

She opened her eyes and found his waiting for her, silver bright. Watching. "Don't," she whispered desperately.

"Don't look at you?" His mouth dipped down again, scolding, teasing. "I want to see. All of you. I want the taste of you, the touch of you. Everything you are, love."

"I'm . . ."

"Tell me."

"Afraid," she whispered.

He shook his head. "Not with me, you're not."

He made her laugh, nibbling at the shell of her ear. He made the room swirl in a vague dark mist when his tongue so gently swirled on her breasts. He made her fingers clench and unclench in his hair, when he roughly cradled her bottom and molded her to him, the friction of skin against skin like the rubbing of metal on flint: fire.

Control . . . was abandoned. He needed her. He wanted her. This was not a man to whom touching was merely a prelude to a physical release. Owen loved to touch. Touching her. Elbows and naval and thighs and throat, it didn't matter. She felt rich as she had never felt rich, yearning as she had never felt it before.

His mouth no longer tasted solely like his, but was also partly her own. His hands skidded over slippery flesh that already belonged to him.

"Owen—"

"We've got to slow down, honey. It's your first time after the baby—" His voice was hoarse, almost harsh.

"I don't care. I don't care..."

He was gentle. She was irritated with him. His invasion was slow, careful, tender ... at least until she wrapped her legs around him, forcing him more deeply inside her. From nowhere she felt his hands suddenly brushing back her hair, his lips like a whisper on hers.

"I've waited a lifetime for you."

He didn't give her a chance to answer. He whispered how he felt inside her, how beautiful he found the soft sounds escaping her lips, how special he found her fire. For a moment, she felt a terrible uncertainty. She didn't know lovemaking as Owen knew it. She needed to give back the richness, the soaring pleasure, the sweet, fierce yearning, but she didn't know how.

She didn't know the rhythm. He caught her. She felt lost and he found her. She felt frantic that it would never end, and then the richness of treasure when he made the whole world explode in passion-drenched softness.

*   *   *

Sunlight danced on Owen's closed eyelids. Laura's gaze slid sleepily over his night beard, the sleepy shadows that softened his eyes, the rumpled spray of dark hair on his forehead. Only when his hand stroked lazily up and down her spine did she realize he was awake.

"You should still be sleeping," he scolded groggily.

"I couldn't."

She was too busy remembering the night before. The first time they'd made love had been all fierce, sharp images, the second all soft, lazy strokes, like silk in firelight.

Wonder was still in her eyes. Desire was a heady champagne, but she hadn't known that until last night. She'd barely slept, didn't want to sleep. Her fingers strayed to his lips, stroking, soft. "You're a beautiful lover."

"So are you, love."

"No. I felt that I was just . . . starting. Trying to know what limbs went where, what to do . . ."

"All the limbs fit. Did you notice?" His teeth nuzzled her fingers, and then stopped, his eyes searching hers. "Are you sore?"

"No."

"You're going to have to open your eyes and look at me if you want me to believe that. You're not suddenly turning modest on me?"

She opened her eyes. His were clear gray, and far too perceptive this early in the morning. "I'm not sore. And modesty wouldn't have a chance for survival around you."

He grinned. "I never could see the point of modesty when nudity is so much fun." A long finger traced the line of her jaw before settling under her chin, tilting her face for him. His kiss was a tender stamp of possession. When he lifted his head, his look was a second stamp. "My beautiful wanton lover," he murmured. "Laura?"

"Hmm?"

He said softly, "I'm sorry—for you—that he was such a fool. But not for me. If he hadn't been part of your life, you might not be with me now. I want you with me. In this bed. In my life. Laura?"

She touched his cheek.

"I'm sorry if I was too rough the first time," he said quietly.

"You weren't."

"I was. And then twice, so soon after the baby..." He shook his head. "The first time, I don't know what happened. I knew you were nervous, and I had every intention of going slow and easy... but then I touched you. And that sparked a small explosion by spontaneous combustion." He touched her nose. "That was partly your doing, love. Because I just didn't believe you wanted anything... contrived. And I didn't want to give you time to think—"

"You certainly didn't give me any time to think," she assured him teasingly.

He gave her a wry look. "You seemed in as much of a hurry as I was."

"I was."

"But still I never meant to be rough. To do anything that might have frightened you . . ."

"You were never too rough," she denied.

"Yes."

"You weren't."

"I was. And you're only arguing because you're dying to leap out of this bed. Some people can lie in bed until noon, but neither of us seems to have cultivated that vice."

She chuckled. "I've always been an instant wake-up type."

"Me, too. And we're going into the city today, remember? That is, if you still want to see how chocolates are made?"

Her eyes blinked wide open then. "Where's the baby? Where are my clothes? And for heaven's sake, where's the coffee?"

Owen burst out laughing and slid out of bed. "And here I thought you loved me for my body."

"That, too." She laughingly bounced away from the hands that reached for her.

She was trying to break the spell of intimacy too fast, bounding out of bed, snatching up her clothes, fleeing for the shower. Part of that was a natural bubble of excitement over the day ahead, some of it was her desire to be ready before the baby woke up. Owen knew that, but also guessed that some of her scurrying around arose from her need to put her clothes on and rebuild those safe walls between them.

He caught up with her in the hall. His body pinned hers securely against the bathroom door, and his fingers tilted up her chin. There weren't going to be any more walls. His mouth pressed down on hers, cool, smooth, and possessive.

He didn't raise his head until her pulse had slowed down and the turquoise in her eyes looked like jewels. "I love you," he said gruffly, and then leaned back, patted her fanny, and turned on a winsome smile. "Let's *go*, woman. I can hardly wait for you to see the business. Think you can control yourself around several hundred pounds of chocolate?"

She let out a breath that was decidedly ragged. "Now, you listen, Reesling. I may have a slight craving for chocolates, but I assure you I'm not going to pounce on them. I'll be a perfect lady."

"God, I hope not."

She opened her mouth, then closed it. Owen burst out laughing.

Her eyes searched his. He'd changed her life the night before. She seemed to have nothing of equal value to give him, and she felt at a loss.

He wanted her, she knew that. He wanted the passionate side of her, and heaven knew he'd proved that. She was conscious that their lovemaking had been one-sided, that he'd done all the giving and asked nothing from her.

She loved him. Enough to want more for him. Enough to question herself honestly as to whether she was woman enough to give him what he needed in a mate.

"Laura?" Owen could have cursed himself, seeing the haunted look in her eyes. What had he said?

She smiled, forcing it. "I was going to ask you to shower with me, but you blew it," she told him sadly. "It's really a shame you teased me about those chocolates . . ."

"I take it back."

"You think I'm a glutton," she accused.

He paused. "In certain areas . . ."

She whipped a towel from the rack and draped it over his head. "That does it." She nearly had the door closed, but his hand snuck in.

She learned a lot about teasing in the shower. In fact, Owen complained bitterly when she stepped out and reached for a towel, but Mari was awake and crying by then.

And Laura had some thinking to do.

- 9 -

"THEN THE PODS ARE cracked open with a machete, and inside, there are from twenty to forty cacao beans. They're white at that time; after they've fermented for a few days, they turn brown. That's when they develop the taste of chocolate." With his hands jammed in the pockets of a white lab coat, Owen paused, an amused grin on his mouth as he watched Laura. "You know, since you asked the question, I assumed you were interested."

"I am, I am." But she couldn't make herself turn her head away from the huge vats.

"After that, they're bagged and shipped here, and then the real fun begins. The beans are put under heat and pressure to get a thick, dark paste called chocolate liquor. You're listening?"

"I'm listening," Laura assured him vaguely.

"Hard chocolate liquor is sold as baking chocolate. If you again put the liquor under pressure, you extract cocoa butter, which is the basis for white chocolate. Mix the fatty cocoa butter with the chocolate liquor, and you have the basis for dark chocolate candy. And it just snowed in the jungles of Brazil."

"Amazing," Laura breathed.

"It snows rainbows down there."

"Does it?"

Owen burst out laughing, swinging an arm around Laura. He leaned closer to whisper, "Go ahead. Stick your finger in. It's obvious you've been longing to do that."

Laura flicked a dreamy glance at Owen, but her eyes immediately returned to the vision in front of her. The bright, long room was filled with huge vats of chocolate. In each, rollers were slowly, hypnotically stirring the lakes of liquid brown. Owen called the stirring process "conching." Laura called it heaven.

The smell invaded every corner of the room, every pore and sensory nerve ending in her skin. She could taste it in the air. "What I'd really like," she said slowly, "is to take off all my clothes and dive in there. Float in it. Swim in it . . . I used to dream about that as a kid. Diving into a sea of chocolate."

Owen's arms slipped around her waist from behind; his lips nuzzled behind her ear. "Lady, don't do that to me," he said huskily. "Now all I can see in my head is this vision of a naked Laura, drenched in chocolate. Turquoise eyes. Gorgeous legs. All of her edible..."

When he turned her, gray eyes met sea-clear blue-green, and held. For a moment, Laura could feel his tongue lapping the imaginary chocolate off, inch by inch. There was no Mari, waiting in his sister's office a few steps away. There was no outside world, where an insistent drizzle had slowed their drive into the city. There was just... Owen, his lips in her hair, the lush pleasure of feeling wanted, and the fragile wonder of knowing that this man not only wanted but demanded every ounce of sensuality she could summon.

She rested her cheek in the hollow of his shoulder, absorbing the strength and warmth of him. A vague malaise had gradually intruded on her conscience, and now it refused to disappear. He'd given everything the night before. He'd given everything since the day they met. What exactly did she have to offer him in return?

Not woman enough. The words had haunted her for a long time. Owen deserved—and expected—a lover as honest and uninhibited as he was. An assertive mate who gave equally. And Laura had been carrying around a lot of emotional baggage that she had to sort through before she felt she had anything to offer him.

Breaking away from him, she feigned a scolding look. "You promised me a visit to the tasting room."

"Testing room," he corrected with a chuckle, but

his eyes narrowed as she bolted for the door. Her abrupt withdrawal, her sudden uneasy silences that morning... "Laura?"

She turned with a smile.

"What's wrong?"

"Nothing, beyond a severe chocoholic attack."

"That we can solve," he said dryly, but didn't believe her.

By some miracle, she didn't drool as they toured the kitchens, but restraint was difficult once they reached the decorating area. Owen's sister Susan joined them with the baby. Tall, with a happy smile and a cap of jet black curls, Susan was as enthusiastic about chocolate as Laura was, and her laughter pealed through the room as she whisked Laura first to one table, then to another.

The women who worked with the candies were dressed in spotless white lab coats. At one table, a worker was dipping cherries in liquid chocolate. At another, several women were squeezing chocolate from pastry guns to produce delicate swirls and rosettes on top of the candies. Laura saw the molds for the whimsical white chocolate unicorns Owen had given her, and for the impossibly delicate cameo. Chocolate-covered strawberries, chocolate-covered jelly beans, caramels... Her hands formed fists in her pockets.

Owen finally leaned toward her, whispering, "Honey, you just weren't cut out to be a martyr. You're also panting in public. Go ahead. That's what they're there for, to taste."

"You don't understand," Laura said glumly. "Once

I start, I might not be able to stop."

"I noticed that last night." He chuckled when a soft rose colored her face, and raised a chocolate-covered cherry to her lips.

Her lips parted helplessly before the morsel of chocolate. It tasted so disgracefully delicious that she couldn't help closing her eyes for a second. When she opened them, Owen's smile had died. He was just looking at her. Not touching.

"Feel the flow of phenylethylamine?" he whispered.

"Pardon?"

"I told you chocolate contained an aphrodisiac. Remember?"

"Yes." Why couldn't she look away from him?

His voice had turned low, gravelly. "Don't you dare try to deny it, Laura. It's far too late for that, for both of us."

"Owen?" Susan hung up the wall phone on the far side of the room and strode toward them. "Gary's been trying to track you down. How about if I take Laura and the baby through packaging and meet you in your office for lunch?"

Owen's eyes searched Laura's, but then lifted, all masked control, to his sister's. "A half-hour then?"

Susan shook her head, watching Owen stride from the room, and then grinned at Laura. "At *last* I've got you alone, you poor woman."

Laura glanced at Owen's sister in surprise.

"I've been elected the family Inquisitor," Susan said cheerfully. "A role I enjoy, actually, since I've always been the biggest gossip in the group. And believe me, the phone lines have been busy from here to Toronto to San Francisco. Suddenly, Owen isn't bellowing around here like the tyrant we all know him to be. Suddenly, he hasn't got his mind on business thirty hours of the day." Susan pushed open the door and led Laura through. "I don't know what you've been doing to our oldest brother, but you're about to be awarded the Reesling's private Nobel Peace Prize. Your baby's been an angel," she added.

"Thank you." Laura, a little bewildered by this news, heard Mari instantly let out a petulant cry.

"Oops! Should I have knocked on wood before I said that?" Susan whispered.

Laura took the baby and said quietly, "I don't actually have any influence over Owen, you know."

Susan shot her a thoughtful look and then changed the subject. "Do you really want to see packaging?"

"What I would really like to do is change Mari's diaper!"

"Come on. We can use Owen's office."

Owen's inner sanctum was a workaholic's dream. Thick rust carpet and paneling absorbed noise; his U-shaped desk was large enough for numerous ongoing projects; and behind it, a computer screen glowed green with the day's action in cocoa futures. *Not* a room where a baby's diaper was normally changed, and then Mari wanted lunch.

Laura settled with the baby in a rust-colored chair in the corner; Susan took the opposite one, kicked off one shoe, and curled a leg under her. Frank and easygoing, she started the conversation again. "We knew there was a woman even before we had your name, you know. The whole family's been taking bets on what you'd look like, what you'd be like. Owen's always been as secretive as a cat. Worms every little escapade out of the rest of us, but never tells us about himself."

"He wouldn't," Laura commented, and again started to say that Susan was misinterpreting her relationship with Owen, but his sister was blithely going on.

"He doesn't open up easily . . . which is why we've all despaired that he'd ever marry. A few women have given him a good chase, but he always slipped the noose." Susan popped a chocolate into her mouth and shook her head. "I've gained five pounds since I've been around here full time. I wish the family manufactured some nice nonfattening product like *shoes*."

Laura chuckled. "I'm a terrible chocoholic."

"Me, too, but not Owen. Owen has a disgusting amount of willpower. Have you noticed?"

"I've noticed," Laura said wryly. "He told me you and Gary had just joined the business?"

Susan nodded. "Gary's got a master's in marketing; he's the brain. I never pretended to be, but Owen bullied me into getting a degree in home economics and chemistry. All I really want to do is work on the recipes. And the patents." She made a face. "Owen insists that's part of my area. Both the recipes and the manufacturing process are patented, but the legal part of the business is strictly boring.

And my older brother is a terrible tyrant."

"So he's confessed."

"Has he?" Susan fingered her hair, a gesture Laura already noticed was habitual. "It's partly true, actually—but not nearly as much as we tease him about. To watch him in action is like watching a symphony conductor—he gives the signals, the rest of us follow, and suddenly there's a smooth flowing business—like music." Susan swung her leg down, slipped on her shoe, and stood up. "He should be coming back. I'll ask Marna if she ordered lunch—you met our office manager? Marna's an angel, puts up with all of us."

"I met her."

"You won't hurt him, will you?"

The words seemed to come from nowhere. Susan was standing at the phone, poised and cool, but there was suddenly a hint of strain on her even features. "He'd kill me for talking to you," she admitted quietly.

"Susan—" But there was no stopping her.

"He needs someone, Laura. Someone who can stand up to him. Someone who can teach him to open up. Someone who's willing to give as much as he does. The thing is, he's always been the one man we could count on. He bandaged our skinned knees and listened to our growing-up problems and served as best man for every wedding. I've always been afraid he would fall into a relationship where he did all the giving." She smiled suddenly, but not with her eyes. "You'd think he never needed anything from anyone, wouldn't you? A very self-sufficient man, our brother—only I've never thought that. He's damned easy to depend on, but I'd like to believe he'll fall in love with woman *he* can depend on, too."

Rain came down in torrents as they were driving home. Mari fell into a fitful nap in her infant seat. Laura was quiet.

Too quiet. Owen stole repeated glances at her pensive profile. "Everything okay?" he asked lightly.

She smiled absently, leaning her head back against the soft leather headrest. "Everything's fine with me, but you're in a lot of hot water, Reesling."

He chuckled. "For any particular reason?"

"You led me to believe the business ran like a well-oiled clock. Good Lord. Between the problems of shipping perishables to market fluctuations to calls from Brazil, there's a disaster a minute there."

"Which is what makes it fun."

"Which means you've managed Grand Central Station alone for too many years," she accused firmly. "Superman should have had it so easy."

"I coached everyone before you got there to make me look good."

She gave him a scolding look. "Considering they all call you a tyrant behind your back, it's a miracle you don't have a constant turnover."

"I beat people who threaten to leave me," he explained, and added quietly, "Could we change the subject?"

"To what?"

"Marriage."

She turned to face him, a catch in her throat. She'd guessed it was coming, but not at this particular moment.

"I don't want to drive you to your place. I want to drive you to my home. I want you with me. Night and day." At a red light, his eyes seared on hers. He hadn't meant to ask her, not here and now. All day he'd felt her gradually withdrawing from him, and the words had just popped out. Now he couldn't seem to stop them. "I love you, Laura. And you know I love your daughter. If you don't feel quite as strongly as I do, I think you will—I know you care. After last night—"

"I more than care," she whispered.

"Then say yes."

Until they reached her drive, she was silent. Owen had made her believe in rainbows again . . . but their whole relationship had been unbalanced. He had done all the giving; she had been a taker. He'd barged into her life, helped her through the roughest weeks she'd ever lived through, stormed her defenses, and turned her into sexual Silly Putty. She loved him. But she'd given him nothing. Everything Susan had said only drilled home her own feelings. *Don't hurt him, will you . . .*

"Laura . . ." He stopped the car in her drive and switched off the key. He was so tense inside he could barely breath. "Look at me."

"I'll do more than look at you." A distinctly feminine smile barely curved her lips. Ignoring all the difficulties of gear shifts and bucket seats, she raised her arms and tugged him closer. She hugged with love, hating anything that caused him to look so tense and wary, needing to feel him close. "I *love* you," she said fervently. "Don't doubt it, Owen, but I need time."

"You don't need time." She smelled like hyacinths and rain, just as she had on the day he met her. His mouth searched for and found hers. "You don't need time to know how you feel when you're with me."

"I know," she agreed huskily, "exactly how I feel when I'm with you."

"Then say yes." His lips hovered over hers, prepared to apply persuasion.

"A few weeks—" His mouth homed in again, wooing her with texture and softness and taste. Last night spun in front of her closed eyes, the silky darkness when she'd waited for him, the fear and anxiety, the reluctance to release control, the burning excitement when she had. She broke free, whispered desperately, "All right. A week—" His hand pushed up her blouse, claimed her taut breast. "You're not being fair—" His tongue drove inside her parted lips, intimately claiming the sweet darkness of her mouth. How could fire be so soft? And more memories danced through her mind, of the feel of the man inside her, of the explosion of a thousand fantasies when the reality of equally wanting and being wanted was so much richer. Equally wanting and being wanted. Equally. There was no love without equal give and take. She broke free again. "Three days, Owen. You have to give me three days. And the baby's crying."

"My princess wouldn't dare cry at this particular moment."

"She is."

Owen drew back, his eyes pure pewter as he studied her. His breathing was low and rasping, his features harsh with tension. "Three days is too long." But her chin was set in that special way of hers, and he sighed. "Then do something for me, Laura," he said quietly. "Don't think—*feel*. And then trust what you feel."

He let her go, against all his better judgment. Every instinct told him not to. Every instinct told him to persuade her by fair means or foul that they belonged together, because something would happen in those three days to keep her from him.

He called each morning at six, and she could hear him sipping his first cup of coffee at the other end of the phone line. By six in the evening, a satin-wrapped package of chocolates had arrived. Wednesday passed and then Thursday. By Friday morning, Laura was bewitched, bedeviled, and anxious.

Owen had never been long on patience.

Laura had worked up a storm, landed several sizable commissions, taken the baby papoose-style on endless walks in the woods, cooked for one, and failed to find the courage to say yes. Or no. She loved him; that was a given. But did she have what it took to make a successful relationship of equals?

There were no answers. *Trust what you feel*, he'd said.

"Well, that's easy to say," she told Mari wearily. Returning from a quick shopping trip, she set the infant seat on the kitchen counter, then wagged her finger at the baby. "Now, don't get into trouble. I just have to bring in the grocery bags."

She brought in two the next trip, and rushed in the door just as the phone rang. Jamming both bags on the counter, she blew back an errant strand of hair and grabbed the phone.

"Laura? I'm less than a mile from your place, and I've got a couple hours free. Could I stop by to see the baby?"

She hesitated. For days, she'd thought only about Owen, and when she thought about Owen, she could almost forget Peter had ever been part of her life. Yet at the sound of her ex-husband's voice, random feelings of anger and hurt clustered in the pit of her stomach, feelings she'd never resolved.

Feelings she'd never faced?

"Laura? Are you there?"

"Yes." She glanced at her watch. "I have an appointment with a local antique dealer in an hour and a half, Peter, and I'd planned to take Mari with me. But if you only want a short visit..."

She barely had the rest of the grocery bags in the house before he pulled into the drive. He stepped out of the car wearing jeans and a denim jacket, and Laura had an odd sensation of *déjà vu*. How many times in her life had Peter climbed out of a car and walked toward her just like that, with the same smile, the same blond hair and masculine good looks? Was there anything in the way he looked or smiled or walked that could have clued her into the cause of their bleak relationship?

"She's grown." He motioned to Mari.

"She grows by the hour," Laura agreed. "I've got iced tea in the kitchen—I'm afraid I'm in the middle of putting away groceries."

"I won't get in your way."

Peter stuffed his hands in his pockets and followed her, at least until they reached the kitchen, where he offered to hold the baby. Laura released the little one and turned back to her groceries. Orange juice, steaks, ice cream—butter pecan. Owen liked butter pecan.

"Your friend's not around?"

"No—you can take her in the other room, if you'd like." Baby lotion, baby shampoo, Q-Tips, diapers. How could one tiny baby's needs fill an entire grocery bag?

"She's falling asleep."

Laura didn't turn around. Opening the freezer, she stacked packages of frozen food. "She usually takes a quick nap about this time of day. There's a playpen in the living room; you can just set her down—tummy down. A blanket's on the side."

"Would you rather do it?"

"Yes." She closed the freezer door, absently rubbing her cold hands on her jeans as she looked at him. "But you can."

He was gone only a moment before he returned to stand in the doorway, this time without the baby. His marvelous blue eyes pinned hers. "You really don't like it when I touch her, do you?"

"I feel protective," Laura admitted, and shrugged. "I'll learn to control it," she said quietly. "You have a right to hold her. And take care of her. And be a father to her, Peter—as long as you don't hurt her." She turned back to unloading brown paper bags. Why on earth had she bought six cans of mushroom soup when she used it so seldom?

Why were her hands suddenly shaking?

"You said you had iced tea. Mind if I pour myself a glass?"

"No, of course not." She removed the soup cans from the spot where she had absently stacked them. Soup cans didn't go next to glasses. Soup cans went down by the tomato sauce—if she could remember where that was. *Face this, Laura. For you . . . for Owen.*

"You've been okay?" Peter asked quietly.

"Fine. You?" His arms bumped hers when he reached for a glass. He didn't move away. Vaguely, Laura tried to remember four years back, to when she trembled with longing for an accidental touch with Peter. All she could recall was wanting to tremble, *wanting* the right kind of love to be there. Which seemed suddenly terribly . . . sad.

"I've been fine. Laura." He hesitated. "I came to see the baby, but most of all I came to talk to you. I've been seeing a therapist." He waited for her to say something, but she didn't. "We talked a lot about you."

She moved to the sink to rinse her hands. Cans were dusty. The air suddenly seemed dusty, yet it was a clear sunny day without a cloud.

"My therapist said . . . I hurt you." Peter's voice suddenly came out in a rush. "I already knew that. What I really came here to tell you was that . . . I never meant to."

When she turned around, he was leaning back against the counter, sunlight glinting on his blond head. Peter had the look of a golden boy, a California surfer, a healthy, wholesome all-American halfback. And he was an artist, a marvelous cellist.

During their marriage, she had always stepped in between Peter and the world whenever he was confronted with something unpleasant. Artists needed to be protected. Golden boys needed sheltering. Only she'd been the victim as well as the guardian. "Then why did you?" she asked evenly.

A quick frown furrowed his brow. "Maybe . . . I didn't know how to handle the problems I had. But at the time—Laura, I really *didn't* meant to hurt you. Or necessarily realize that I was."

"Know something?" Laura said slowly. "That's not good enough."

He drew in a long breath. "Look. I didn't choose to be bi. I know you're hung up on that—"

"No," she said swiftly. "It was a shock—but that wasn't what hurt, Peter. It was your cutting me down. Hitting below the belt. Trying to make me ashamed for . . . feeling." Leaning back against the stove, she raked her fingers through her hair distractedly. *"Why?"* she whispered. "Why couldn't you simply have been honest with me? Told me what you were feeling—or at least tried?"

"Because you'd have left me," Peter lashed back.

She stared at him, seeing something in Peter's face, in his eyes, she'd never seen before. The phone rang suddenly, a jarring sound in the still room. When Laura didn't immediately answer it, Peter lifted the receiver. "Yes?" he clipped out. His eyes were blue chips as he handed it to her.

Owen's tone was cool. "If I'd known he was there . . . Laura, if he's come over there to give you a hard time again—"

"No. No," she repeated more softly, and oddly wasn't sure whether to laugh or cry. His voice was ballast. He was Gibraltar. She took a breath, and clean, pure air filled her lungs. "Owen, I'll call you back. I promise—within an hour." She glanced at her watch. "No, I'll be gone later. I'll call around dinner time."

She hung up, regretfully aware that she'd cut Owen off, but Peter was still leaning against the counter, and she wanted the unfinished business with him over and done with.

"You're serious about him, aren't you?" Peter lifted the iced-tea glass to his lips and took a long draft. "You don't have to answer that. I always knew you would leave me for someone else sooner or later."

Laura shook her head. "You're not making sense," she said gently. "You didn't want me, Peter. You made that very plain. So why on earth would you have cared if I *had* left you?"

He raised the glass, and studied the gleam of the amber liquid in the sunlight, then set it down and walked to the door. "I loved you," he said quietly.

"In my own way, Laura. Don't doubt that. And I held you as long as I could . . . the only way I knew how."

"Peter?"

But he kept on walking, through the kitchen and hall, then outside toward his car. Laura followed him as far as the front door. Leaning against the doorjamb, she watched his car back up and disappear down the long drive. When he was gone, she closed her eyes in sudden weariness.

So much hurt, so much anger, so many confused feelings . . . She'd wanted answers from Peter. And gotten half of them. Gradually, she understood that she'd had the rest of those answers inside herself all the time.

He said that he'd held her as long as he could, the only way he knew how . . . and that he'd loved her. Laura had always known he cared—which was why it was so difficult to understand why he'd deliberately used guilt and shame to hurt her. He'd given her that answer.

Guilt *had* kept her with him, much longer than she should have stayed in the marriage. He made me a victim, Laura thought fleetingly. When she heard stories about wife abuse, she'd never understood why a woman stayed with a man who hurt her. Peter had never physically harmed Laura, but she suddenly understood the whole syndrome very well. A woman could be made to believe that she was responsible for a bad marriage, that she was the source of the problems, and that she deserved the blame.

She'd believed that.

No more.

Long-buried anger and hurt surfaced and dissipated like an early morning fog. Her anger wasn't at Peter but at herself. He wasn't evil and he wasn't a bastard. Real people were never one-dimensional. Peter was simply a lonely and unhappy man . . . but his troubles weren't hers. Owen had said it, so very gently. How long was she going to stand around and pay for Peter's problems?

How long before she found the courage to demand what she wanted and needed in her life? And to believe she had a right to those things?

In the playpen, Mari let out a sharp cry. Not a wail, not a tantrum yell, just a conversational I'm-awake-Mom whimper. Laura smiled and hurried into the living room. She picked up her daughter, holding and hugging and loving her.

Before she sat down to nurse the infant, she took the phone off the hook. After the baby had been fed, she would take her to the antique dealer's. And absolutely as soon as possible, she was desperate to see Owen.

But for now, just for a few moments, she needed silence. And her daughter. And in a curious way, herself.

- 10 -

". . . You can't get the Lear ready faster than that?
No . . . Hell, I understand that. Midnight then,
Stover." Owen hung up the phone, tossed his reading glasses on the desk, and irritably rubbed the
bridge of his nose.

He'd barely slept in the last three nights.

Leaning forward, he picked up the phone and
dialed Laura's number again. Busy. It had been busy
for four hours; she had taken it off the hook. And
that bastard of an ex-husband had been there. Tilting
back his chair, Owen stared bleakly at a sun-dazzled
landscape and saw none of it.

Dread tied a knot in his stomach. It was after
seven. She wasn't still making business calls. She'd

taken the phone off the hook for privacy.

She didn't want to talk to anyone.

Correction. She didn't want to talk to him.

Added to her ex-husband's visit—he should have murdered the guy in the first place—and three days of intolerable waiting, he couldn't deny he might have pushed too hard; loved too hard on that one very special night . . . Dammit, he didn't know what he'd done wrong. He didn't *care* what he'd done wrong. If he'd lost control making love to her, it was because she was so damned responsive. And loving. And the only woman on earth with whom he'd ever dreamed he'd lose control.

Owen lurched out of the chair, paced for all of five minutes, and then bolted up the stairs. A half-hour later, he bolted back down, carrying a suitcase and looking grim. For three days, he'd had an idea of what to do if Laura said no. It wasn't a good idea. He even had the feeling it was a half-baked, out-of-control, harebrained idea, which wasn't like him . . . but at the moment he was feeling half-baked and out of control.

He was going to be on a plane at midnight.

So was Laura.

Humming, Laura finished folding the laundry . . . and jumped when her front door clattered open to reveal a tall, dark man in jeans, walking boots, and red crew-neck sweater. He looked remarkably intent on breaking something . . . if the set of his jaw and the glint in his pewter gray eyes were any indication.

She tilted her head. "Owen?"

He stalked over to the phone, lifted the receiver, and dropped it back on the hook. "Afraid someone would call?"

Her brows fluttered up. "I forgot it was still off the hook."

"He's gone?"

"Who's gone?" She frowned. "You mean Peter?"

"Where's the baby?"

"The baby?"

"Laura!"

"You're being a little confusing," she said delicately. "Can I have a hug and kiss, or do you just want to keep on yelling for no reason in particular?"

Owen sighed. "Do you have any suitcases?"

"Sure. I also have toothpicks. Shoes. Lamps. And the things most people have."

"Where?"

"Which thing?"

"The suitcases."

"In the closet upstairs. Any particular reason?"

"Because you're going with me to Brazil. Mari's going, too."

She digested this, read all the anxiety and exhaustion in his face, and didn't really need to know more. "All right."

"Do me a favor and don't argue. Not on this, Laura."

"I wasn't," she said mildly, and then obligingly followed him up the stairs, since he seemed to be through talking downstairs. Owen in a temper was ... interesting. She expected most women would find him awesome and intimidating ... but then, most women, thank God, hadn't made love with Owen.

Some. Some must have. Those she'd been wondering about for the last few hours since Peter had left.

All of them might have been dynamite in bed . . . but none of them had had the brains to hold on to him. She'd screwed her head on very straight in the last few hours. She'd had one rotten relationship, and had tried very hard to turn it into a lifelong trauma. Actually, being rejected for another man was probably worth a lifelong trauma, if one had the time for it.

She didn't. Not anymore. It wasn't Peter's fault that she'd forgotten exactly what she had to offer in a relationship. Herself. A woman who could stand on her own. A woman capable of a deep and enduring love. Owen wasn't getting away. And she'd tell him that . . . as soon as he gave her the chance.

At the moment, he was bouncing suitcases on her bed, flipping them open, and jerking open drawers. He tossed one lace camisole into the suitcase. Powder pink. Then a second one in oyster. Three pairs of underpants. He closed the drawer on her bras without packing any.

She cleared her throat. Braless was okay, but she really didn't want to sag before she was thirty. "Actually, I'm capable of packing my own things," she mentioned.

"I will." His head whipped up. "Dammit. You do have a valid passport?"

She smiled. "Since I was six. I told you, my family traveled a lot."

He rubbed the nape of his neck distractedly. "I'd worked out Mari, figuring she couldn't possibly have one. I'll need her birth certificate; I've got a temporary passport and visa waiting for her. But *you*—I'd counted on you having one. And I shouldn't have. I should have made absolutely sure..." He stopped again, shooting her another gray look. "Laura, you *can* leave your work for a few days?"

For a man radiating don't-argue-with-me, he was remarkably anxious. Vulnerable, she thought lovingly. It was the first time she'd seen Owen vulnerable. "I don't have anything that won't wait a few days, given a phone call or two."

"You can make phone calls from Bahia; that's not a problem. Mari—"

"Is sleeping."

"We'll wake her up at the last minute."

"Do you want a drink?"

"No."

"Do you want to tell me what's wrong?"

"I want you *with* me. That's what's wrong." He lifted his head long enough to glare at her. "Laura. What did he say to you?"

For an instant, she was busy absorbing the look in his eyes. Need. Bold and stark. And just for her. Belatedly, she remembered his question. "What did *who* say to me?"

"Never mind. You'll talk in Brazil. Believe me, you'll talk in Brazil."

Two days later, Laura was leaning over a second-story wrought-iron balcony, gazing at the Brazilian countryside. Below was a rolling green landscape, but very different from Connecticut's fresh green crispness in summer. This was a tropical emerald, all lush and tangled, exotic and wild wherever man hadn't made efforts to control it.

The Reesling plantation was well controlled. To the east, Owen's cacao trees stretched in neat rows as far as the eye could see. One would never guess the cacao groves had any relationship to chocolate. The trees were strangely shaped, the trunks curved and warped looking. The cacao itself grew even more oddly. Yellow, red, and green, the pods looked like summer squash clinging to the tree trunks.

Inside those pods were the beans, thirty and forty in a cluster. Once the pods were cracked open with a machete, one could sample those whitish nuggets—and begin to understand the remote relationship between nature's creation and the thirty-dollar-a-pound delectable treats that Owen made from it. In this case, humanity's work had it all over nature's—and Laura felt qualified to judge, having spent several hours crouched on the ground, surrounded by brown-skinned workers' children who were delighted to show her how to crack open the pods.

Overall, it was a damned good place for an ardent chocoholic to be abducted to. It might even be a perfect place, if her kidnapper would show up.

Owen had brought her here, and then seemed to go into hiding. On the surface, of course, he had excuses. Since he rarely visited Bahia, it was natural that Senhor Montez would want to whisk him around, show Owen what a fantastic job he was doing as a manager, and lay a list of problems on him. Labor, irrigation, transportation, weather... When Senhor Montez didn't get excited, he talked English, so Laura caught the gist of the frequent crises a cacao-plantation manager confronted.

That was on the surface, though. Beneath that, Owen was proving elusive. Laura figured he was ashamed of himself. He should be. For openers, kidnapping was a federal offense. Besides that, he'd behaved in a particularly high-handed fashion, and Laura wasn't at all surprised that he was reluctant to face her.

Turning around, she wandered back inside from the balcony, casting a wistful glance at the bed. It was a marvelous bed, big and old, with four tall posts of gleaming mahogany, and drapes of netting that reminded her of the Sleeping Beauty fairy tale. Two people had slept in that bed for the last two nights, but the poor bed wasn't seeing any action. Owen was going to sleep unbelievably late and getting up unbelievably early.

"Senhora Anderson?"

A short, dark woman appeared in the doorway, carrying Mari. Dressed in black, with huge black eyes and warm brown skin, Senhora Montez had proved welcoming and friendly from the first minute she'd spotted the baby.

"She woke? I didn't hear her." Smiling, Laura reached for Mari, but the little woman shook her head.

"No, no. I take her out for fresh air... if you

don't mind? Not in the sun, and not too hot, promise. I take very good care..." With a quick, beaming smile, she disappeared.

Laura sighed ruefully. Getting her hands on her own baby was proving almost as difficult as getting her hands on Owen. Blond babies seemed to be at a premium in Brazil. Mari was brought to her at feeding time; other than that, the little one didn't have the chance to whimper before someone in the household picked her up.

Laura had a sneaky suspicion that Owen had arranged part of that baby care to give her a rest. It would be just like him, and she had to admit it was nice being spoiled. Actually, the last two days had been a comprehensive experience in being spoiled. Clean clothes miraculously appeared in her closet; the sheets were ironed; drinks and snacks appeared in front of her before she realized she wanted them; the baby was taken care of, and quiet arranged in the afternoon so Laura could rest.

Hands in the wide pockets of her white cotton skirt, Laura wandered into the hall and down the wide, banistered stairs. She was feeling almost annoyingly well rested... and slightly unnerved.

She needed Owen, for two reasons. One was to—gently and figuratively—bring him to his knees. He needed to understand that she neither expected nor wanted a Superman. He needed to learn that she was capable of assertively, demandingly giving back.

And the second thing she needed him for was to seduce him. Take all the initiative, throw away the

last of her inhibitions, and show him the full force
of the wanton side to her that Peter had continually
cut down.

She was going to do both, with her chin up and
all flags flying. She loved that man. He was worth
climbing mountains for.

It would just be slightly easier if she could find
him. And if she weren't scared witless. She knew
what she had to do, what she wanted and needed
to do to put their relationship on an equal footing,
but talk was so easy. This was the gambler's last
poker hand, the skydiver's last jump. Owen might
not expect more of her than she'd shown him so
far, but Laura expected more of herself.

Owen took the back stairs two at a time. Upstairs,
he dropped his sweat-stained shirt and khakis in a
pile, then ducked into the shower and flicked on
the faucets. He grimaced. He could buy the luxury
of hot water, but no amount of money could produce
water pressure in Bahia.

Still, eventually the soft, hot stream rinsed the
dirt and grime from his body. He'd spent the day
in the drying sheds, analyzing the practicality of
new equipment with Montez. Paulo liked to spend
his money. The subject had come up before and was
truthfully a serious issue that deserved his time, but
Owen knew well they could have discussed it on
the telephone between New York and Brazil.

He was avoiding Laura. Keeping a low profile
didn't come naturally to him; it just seemed something he'd taken up in the last two days. He'd pressed

her into a relationship, pressed her into sleeping with him, pressed her to making a lifelong commitment, and had now kidnapped her. Dammit, she had a right to time and space. He'd given her virtually none. From the moment he'd met her, he'd just been so damned afraid of losing her...

And still was.

She couldn't very well say no if she couldn't catch up with him.

On the other hand, he couldn't stay away from her much longer. When he did see her, he planned to be loving, calm, understanding, patient, rational, and apologetic. In his heart, he was dismally certain that he would find some method more wild than kidnapping if she said no.

Either way, making love to her seemed the best way to start. Flipping off the shower faucets, he reached out blindly for a towel and mopped the dripping water from his face and hair.

Once he could see, he started roughly toweling his back... until he felt a cool draft from the doorway. Looking up, he froze.

Laura was dressed in red. Laura never dressed in red. The color all but said Hello, sexy. She was barefoot and barelegged; the smocked dress was Brazilian peasant style, gathered loosely—perilously loosely—at the bodice. Her cheeks were flushed, her eyes subtly darkened with mascara, and her hair fell in a satin swirl to her shoulders. As his eyes traveled from her toes to her head, he caught a whiff of her perfume and stopped breathing.

The scent was lethally effective. Quickly wrapping a towel around his waist, he said weakly, "Hi."

"Hi."

He hadn't seen that gleam in her eyes before. Actually, it was less a gleam than a . . . sizzle. Owen tried out a casual "Mari in bed?"

"Mari's fed, bathed, and in bed for the night."

"Hmmm." Behind her, he noted that the door to the bedroom had been closed. And next to the four-poster bed were two chairs and a table—he caught a glimpse of an open bottle of wine and two glasses.

"Did you catch dinner? I meant to be in by seven, but—"

"I know. Senhor Montez had another crisis for you to handle. And yes, I've had dinner."

She didn't sound irritated. Owen snatched another towel to dry off his chest, never taking his eyes off Laura. She was sending him mixed messages. One was loud and clear. She was a beautiful, infinitely desirable woman, nothing Owen didn't already know, but it was a pleasure to see her acknowledge it. The second message was rather alarming. Laura vibrated determination. Determination and sensuality didn't usually go together.

It was then Owen noticed that her hands were trembling. Another glance told him that her lower lip was trembling too. And that behind the sizzle in her eyes lay a huge well of emotion she was trying very hard to hide from him.

Owen was perplexed, but he also relaxed.

Not so Laura. "Owen, we're gong to have a little talk," she said firmly.

"It's past time," he agreed.

"We're going to talk about kidnappers. And men who drug helpless women with chocolates. And men who take babies to candlelit dinners. And men who totally desert women, leaving them for two days on their own—"

"Laura, about the last two days—"

"Out." With a severe expression, Laura motioned him into the other room. The towel still draped around his waist, Owen obediently trailed into the bedroom, taking one short detour to make sure the door was locked. She pointed to the bed. He sat.

At that point, Laura would have lost courage, if he hadn't been sitting there with a love glow in his eyes. Instead, the longer he looked, the more momentum she gained. She moved closer, much closer. Close enough to breathe the scent of him, close enough to see his eyes turn pure dusky pewter in reaction to her nearness, close enough to slowly unknot the towel at his waist. When he was naked, he tossed the towel to the other side of the room.

"Two can play this game, you know," he remarked.

"If I were in as much trouble as you are, I wouldn't be talking," she advised.

Mute, he leaned back on the bed like a man very sure of who he was and what he wanted . . . and of what she was going to do next. Pagan gods should look so damned sure of themselves. And that wouldn't do at all, Laura thought fleetingly. Maybe he'd caught on that she was a little nervous? She could have sworn it didn't show.

"Come here, love," he whispered.

"I'll come, but don't touch," she warned. "Agreed?"

His smile held both amusement and surprise, but he nodded, staring with undisguised interest as she pulled off her sash, then slowly peeled the dress over her head. When the garment was a puddle on the floor, he was no longer smiling. She wasn't wearing anything beneath it.

"Come here," he repeated.

She shook her head. "Only if you promise not to touch."

"I'll promise anything you want. Just come here."

He still didn't understand. He certainly thought he did, because when he knelt on the bed, he tried to reach for her. She had to firmly motion his hands away. "Please?" she said softly.

"Laura—"

"Just lie back."

When he pushed a pillow behind his head, Laura knelt next to him. He'd taught her any number of things the night they'd made love. One was that one could make love with eyes alone, and her eyes were brazen, intimately lingering over his legs, his hips, his furred chest, the slope of his shoulders.

Owen stayed still, watching her face. A faint breeze stirred the draperies at the window, catching a strand or two of her hair, curling it around her flushed cheeks. He was more than willing to play any game she wanted to and make love any way she wanted to, yet after a time he felt the unfamiliar tension in his limbs, a sweep of color on his skin. He'd never had a modest bone in his body, and—

although he knew he was fit—no vanity about the
way he was built.

As Laura studied him, he suddenly became conscious of his body in a different way. He'd sought
pleasure in simply looking at her, but it was oddly
unnerving to have her seek it the same way. He felt
vulnerable. Not a word he accepted easily for himself. "Laura."

She leaned forward. Her fingertips stroked first;
her caress was light and those fingers trembling.
Her hair swung in a curtain around her face as she
learned his skin, learned what made his pulse
quicken, his flesh darken, his body tense with desire. She learned Owen as a woman has a right and
a need to know her mate.

Her touch changed. She used her palms to stroke
from his throat to his shoulders, down his thighs
and calves. She tried friction and then softness,
kneading and then slow, teasing caresses.

And then firmly put Owen's wandering hands
back at his sides.

Seducing, she was discovering, took the utmost
concentration. Owen wasn't an easy man to reduce
to Silly Putty. She wasn't surprised at that, but she
hadn't counted on him becoming more tense instead
of less.

She tried her tongue. His nipples hardened like
tiny little knots when she licked them. His naval
contracted, and when her tongue made a loving
circle lower, she discovered that Owen, with star-
tling speed, went totally out of control.

Again, she pushed his hands back to his sides

and raised her eyes to his. "I want you to relax," she chided softly.

"Honey, there isn't a prayer of that. You're no longer," he said thickly, "shy."

"I'm afraid I was never shy," she admitted.

Her smile was pure wicked temptress one instant, as innocent as a child's the next. He felt the full force of woman turned on him, from the sway of her breasts to the soft darts of her tongue to her whispered breath deliberately teasing him. She knelt over him, brushing her breasts over his chest, touching nipple to nipple. She tried her teeth, taking small nips from his shoulder and throat.

Pleasure skidded up and down his bloodstream. Desire heated his skin. He wanted to give; she was forcing him to take. The sensation was new and almost... frightening. Laura had powers over him he'd given to no other person, powers he was just beginning to understand. Powers he was afraid she understood all too well.

"Laura..." He reached for her again, but this time she was already there, her softness curled around him, her lips hovering over his.

"You taught me honesty," she whispered. "But it has to be the same for both of us, love. I need you, Owen, I freely admit it. But I have to know you need me, too. I don't want a hero to slay dragons for me. I want a man who's as vulnerable in love as I am."

"You doubted that?" Rapidly, with infinite gentleness, he switched positions so she was pinned beneath him, her hair fanned out on the pillow. His fingers reached out to touch the silky strands, lingering there. "I've been scared as hell from the moment I met you. How could you not know? I've never needed anyone the way I need you." His fingertip traced the shape of her soft, warm lips. "Be with me," he said huskily. "Love with me, live with me. Fight with me, I don't care. Just don't leave me . . ."

Her eyes closed, with kiss after kiss. Darkness spiraled around her. His body was trembling, dampness making a satin sheen on his shoulders and chest. She had a crazy image in her head of a thousand swallows set free from a church belfry. Love was exploding inside her, soaring high, and that sky was so big and blue.

She shouted his name.

He whispered hers.

"Owen?"

"Hmmm?"

"There's no possible way I can sleep with your hand there."

"Are you sleepy?"

Her lashes fluttered open. The room was dark except for the rays of a pale moon in the window. And the dark glow from Owen's eyes just above hers. "You *must* be tired."

"I am. A little. But I want my yes." He brushed kiss after kiss on lips that were already swollen and tender.

"A yes to what?" she murmured in surprise.

"To marrying me."

"I certainly thought I made it very clear how I felt about spending my life with you."

"Not clear enough." He slid his palm down under the sheet again. "You're not going to sleep until I have a very clear black-and-white yes."

"You have no intention of letting me sleep anyway."

"True." He looked down at her for a long time, at her cheeks and chin and nose and brows and lips. Each feature was perfect. "I didn't expect to find you," he said gravely. "I've always been alone; I've never been afraid of being alone. I thought I was happy until I met you, Laura. I don't need anyone to serve me dinner or put up with my temper or dust my house. I need you to come home to. I feel free to be honest with you, to show you the faults as well as the good stuff. I need you while I grow and change, and maybe falter and fail. With you I can be vulnerable now and then—you used that word. I *need* you, love."

His eyes were a sheen of silver. Her own were blurred with tears. "I thought you'd changed my life," she whispered. "But that wasn't right, Owen, because real change has to come from inside, and it's a lonely process. I want you there, as I change. I want your children. I want to grow old with you. I want to be shy and wanton, self-sufficient and insecure, business lady and sultry temptress . . . with you . . ."

He trapped her in a tangle of arms and legs, leveling a kiss of love on the perfect mold of her lips. "Say it, love."

"When they said you were a tyrant, I never believed them—"

"If you ever want a chocolate again as long as you live—"

Her eyes widened. *"Yes. Yes. Yes."*

A long time later, she murmured in his ear. "You know, it has nothing to do with chocolates."

"I know."

"But whatever you do, don't let your sister talk you into going into the shoe business."

Owen burst out laughing.

"You think that's funny?"

"I think"—sleepily Owen pinned her closer—"you're looking for trouble again."

"I couldn't be. The sun's nearly up. We *have* to get some sleep."

"I love you, Laura."

She reached for him. "We can catch up on our sleep next year," she agreed.

SECOND CHANCE AT LOVE

Be Sure to Read These New Releases!

THE FIRE WITHIN #304 by Laine Allen
Ecstasy turns to rage, tenderness to torment,
when Cara Chandler's secrets...and Lou Capelli's
suspicions...twist their whirlwind marriage
into a sham of wedded bliss!

WHISPERS OF AN AUTUMN DAY #305 by Lee Williams
Adam Brady has "stolen" her famous
grandfather's love letters, and Lauri Fields *must*
get them back—no matter what deceptive...
or seductive...measures she must take!

SHADY LADY #306 by Jan Mathews
Catherine Coulton intends to arrest the man for
solicitation—instead she finds herself locked in his hungry
embrace! Then she learns he's Nick Samuels,
infamous womanizer...*and* celebrated vice-squad cop!

TENDER IS THE NIGHT #307 by Helen Carter
Popular Toni Kendall clashes with
possessive Chris Carpenter from their first
explosive encounter—though his take-charge
manner attests to a strength she can't resist!

FOR LOVE OF MIKE #308 by Courtney Ryan
Hours after jilting her fiancé, Gabby
Cates is stranded on a deserted beach in a bedraggled
wedding gown, with her cat, her guilty
conscience...and slightly intoxicated, thoroughly
spellbinding Mike Hyatt...

TWO IN A HUDDLE #309 by Diana Morgan
Dynamite quarterback Trader O'Neill
knows all the right moves. But Selena Derringer,
reluctant owner of the *worst* football
team, wonders if he's offering a lasting commitment
or merely masterful game playing...

Order on opposite page

SECOND CHANCE AT LOVE

·COMING NEXT MONTH

Highly Acclaimed
Historical Romances From Berkley

_____ 07691-9 **Dawn of the White Rose**
$3.95 by Mary Pershall

"Five stars. A must." — <u>Affaire de Coeur</u>
From the author of the nationwide best seller <u>A Shield of Roses</u>
comes a new novel about two lovers caught in a struggle where
surrender means love.

_____ 08075-7 **Silver Clouds, Golden Dreams**
$3.95 by Theresa Conway

With all the drama, suspense, and passionate abandon that
made <u>Paloma</u> a bestseller, Theresa Conway creates a
magnificent new saga of courage and faith — as one brave family
struggles to rebuild their lives in a brand new land.

_____ 08395-0 **Scarlet and Gold**
$7.95 by Ellen Tanner Marsh
(A Berkley Trade Paperback)

From the <u>New York Times</u> bestselling author of <u>Wrap Me in
Splendor</u> comes the dramatic tale of wild, beautiful Athena
Courtland and the silver-eyed sailor whose soul raged with
desire from the first moment he saw her.

_____ 08472-8 **Love, Honor and Betray**
$4.50 by Elizabeth Kary

"A great love story, charged with emotion...These two lovers
will not soon be forgotten..." — Johanna Lindsey
"Thrilling and evocative...a page-turner!" — Roberta Gellis

Prices may be slightly higher in Canada.

432